Studies of
THE NEW YORK ACADEMY OF MEDICINE
COMMITTEE ON MEDICINE AND
THE CHANGING ORDER

GOVERNMENT IN PUBLIC HEALTH

LONDON
HUMPHREY MILFORD
OXFORD UNIVERSITY PRESS

An Act for the More Effectual Preventing the Spreading of Contagious Distempers.

Whereas great Numbers of the Inhabitants of this Province have been Destroyed by Malignant, Contagious Diseases Brought here from Africa and other parts of America to Prevent which, as much as may be, for the time to come **Be it Enacted** by the Pallatyne, and the Rest of the True and Absolute Lords, Proprietors of Carolina To geather with the advice and Consent of the Members of the Generall Assembly now mett at Charles Towne for the South West part of this Province And it is hereby Enacted by the Authority of the Same, that from and after the Ratification of this Act, that Gilbert Guttery, Shall be a Commissioner for Enquireing into the State of health of all Such persons as Shall be aboard Any Ship or Vessell Arriveing in this Province.

Be it further Enacted by the Authority aforesaid that the Commissioner aforesaid Shall have Power, and he is hereby Impowred, and Required to go on board of all Ships and Other Tradeing Vessells as Soon as they come over the Barr, and make Strict, and Diligent Enquiry into the State of health of that Place from whence such Vessell Last, his Likewise of all those persons who are now On board, and into the Cause of the Death of Such as have Dyed On board the Said Shipp (if any) Dureing the Voyage and Shall Make Such Searches betwixt Decks or in Other Places of the Vessell as he shall think Necessary for finding Out the truth and Shall Likewise Order all the Men to be brought upon Deck the better to be Seen, and Observed for the Same purpose.

Be it further Enacted by the Authority aforesaid, That the Commissioner Aforesaid Shall have Power and he is hereby Impowred, and Required to Administer an Oath to the Master, and One Or two Seaman more of Every Ship for Discovering the State of health of those On board, Dureing the Voyage, and at that present time Particularly why have Dyed, or are now Sick On board, and of what Disease, and it is hereby Enacted by the Authority aforesaid that if the Commissioner upon Examination findes Cause to Send any person then On board, A Shore to the Pest House, the Master of the Said Vessell Shall Send them there, and Shall Cleanse the Vessell and the Cloaths and Other things that are On board after Such Manner as he Shall be Directed by the Commissioner above Mentioned.

Be it further Enacted by the Authority aforesaid, that if it appear to the Commissioner above mentioned upon Examination that Any person On board the Said Ship is Sick of the Plague, Small Pox, Spotted Feavour, Flam Distemper, Guinea Feavour, Or any other Malignant Contagious Disease, or that any person Dureing the present Voyage, hath Dyed from On board the Said Ship, of any of those Distempers, aforesaid, he then Shall Order the Master, or Commander, of the Said Vessell to Send all Such persons, then On board, or who May after that become Sick On Shoar to the Pest House On Sullivants Island. Shall Order the Master or Commander afore said to Lye with his Ship at Anchor, without Sending his boat a Shoar, Except to Sullivants Island, nor Suffer Any to come On board his Said Vessell from Any Place of this Province Dureing the Space of Twenty Dayes after those Orders are Given, Dureing which time the Master or Commander is hereby Required to have his Ship, and things On board to be Cleansed, after such Manner as by the Said Commissioner is directed,

APPOINTMENT OF A HEALTH OFFICER

Act of the General Assembly of the Province of Carolina, June 7, 1712

Government in Public Health

HARRY S. MUSTARD, B.S., M.D., LL.D. *1889-1966.*

DeLamar Professor of Public Health Practice and Director,
School of Public Health, Faculty of Medicine,
Columbia University

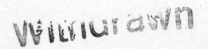
NEW YORK

THE COMMONWEALTH FUND

1945

PUBLISHED BY THE COMMONWEALTH FUND
41 EAST 57TH STREET, NEW YORK 22, N.Y.

PRINTED IN THE UNITED STATES OF AMERICA
BY E. L. HILDRETH & COMPANY, INC.

FOREWORD

THE Committee on Medicine and the Changing Order was established by the Council of The New York Academy of Medicine in the winter of 1942 and began its work in February, 1943. This action was taken in the conviction that the medical profession is confronted by problems which require thorough study, and that the Academy had both the opportunity and the responsibility to contribute to the effective solution of these problems.

The Council's instructions to the Committee were to review the nature, quality, and direction of the economic and social changes that are taking place now and that are to be anticipated in the immediate future; to define in particular how these changes are likely to affect medicine in its various segments; to determine how the best elements in the science and art of medicine and in its service to the public may be preserved, embodied, and extended in whatever new social patterns may ultimately appear.

The objectives of the Committee were defined as follows:

To explore the possibilities and to formulate methods of maintaining and improving standards of quality in medical service, including medical research, medical education, the maintenance of health, both physical and mental, the prevention of disease, and the treatment of disease.

To study the means of making available to larger groups of people and to the country as a whole the best known practice in preventive and curative medicine.

To explore the possibilities and to formulate proposals of distributing these services not only to a larger number but also at a lower per capita cost than the present system permits.

The Committee was composed of physicians, representatives of the allied professions of dentistry and nursing, and laymen. The physicians were chosen because of their special interest and experi-

ence in medical education, public health, or social medicine and
welfare, as well as for their wide experience in the practice of medicine. Membership was not restricted to physicians who were Fel-
lows of the Academy.

Since laymen, as the recipients of medical service, are vitally concerned in its development and distribution, it was considered important to have them represented on the Committee. Members
from the laity were therefore selected, representing labor, industry,
law, social work, and the clergy. The individuals chosen were those
particularly interested in the problems of health, preventive medicine, and social welfare.

The Committee's work has involved a number of concurrent activities. It has held weekly meetings at which experts from such
varied fields as economics, politics, industry, labor, medicine, dentistry, the hospitals, nursing, and social work, addressed the Committee, presenting in their discussion the basic data of their respective interests and interpretations of the significant social and
economic changes that were being witnessed and that could be anticipated. These discussions were naturally related to medicine and
medical service and afforded the Committee the opportunity to
take testimony and to orient itself to the different aspects of the
problems which it was studying.

Being acutely aware of the need for orderly, systematic, and objective data relative to the many aspects of medical education,
medical research, and medical service, the Committee early enlisted the cooperation of a number of experts in the composition
of a series of monographs devoted to the major medical problems
of today. These monographs are designed to provide the framework for an understanding of the current medical situation and its
trends. Contemporary medicine is treated as a product of evolution. The monographs are historical in character; they are not
chronological recitations, but show rather the reciprocal effects of

medicine and the technical, social, economic, and political changes that have taken place in American life.

This treatment of the subject-matter brings to light not only the achievements but also the inadequacies in present-day medical practice—the uneven development of its different sectors, the prevailing incongruities and irrationalities, as well as the lag in the adjustment of medicine to the social needs of today. The monographs therefore offer not only a survey of the present situation but also an analysis of how it came to be and some indications as to future trends.

In addition to the monographs, the Committee will issue a report, representing the conclusions drawn from its deliberation and studies.

The Committee has selected for the authors of its monographs recognized experts and has afforded them full freedom in their work. While, therefore, the monographs form an integral part of the Committee's studies, their publication does not necessarily imply the Committee's endorsement of statements of fact or opinion which are entirely the responsibility of the authors.

PREFACE

In this monograph, Dr. Mustard brings out the rapid extension of the field of public health as one of the important trends in modern medicine. Recognizing that public health activity originated as a local responsibility, Dr. Mustard describes the growing interest on the part of the state and federal governments and, in so doing, faces squarely the present trend toward increased federal control through the Public Health Service. He also makes clear that this trend may be ascribed in large part to the lack of efficiency at the local level where, in many communities, either the leadership or the public support was inferior to that available to the Public Health Service. The fact that basic public health services are as yet by no means available to all communities in the country is to Dr. Mustard the immediate challenge to the Public Health Service and he raises the question whether, until that challenge is met, the time is ripe to consider nation-wide activities in new and highly specialized lines.

Turning to the organization and activities of state health departments, Dr. Mustard traces their natural development and describes their proper sphere of action. He also very clearly indicates the recently increased responsibility of state administrators as intermediaries between the federal and local authorities in the distribution of funds appropriated as grants-in-aid from the federal to the local governments, and points out the trend toward an increase of such grants in the future.

Dr. Mustard, of course, recognizes the fact that the bulk of actual health service must be administered at the local level, and pleads for a better appreciation of this fact by the citizens of each community. Public health authorities in a democracy can function adequately only if they have the cooperation and support of the general public, and he particularly emphasizes the responsibility of physicians in this regard, and urges the wider application of preventive measures in medical practice and a more whole-hearted support of the public health authorities.

The general picture which Dr. Mustard portrays, while constructively critical, is by no means pessimistic. In giving credit to what has been accomplished, he urges that a basically sound program, founded on proven knowledge, is the factor of prime importance, and strongly emphasizes our reliance upon continued scientific research, much of which is a definite government responsibility. As a basis for discussion, if not for immediate action, Dr. Mustard suggests a plan for the financial support of the public health program by an equal division of responsibility between the federal, state, and local governments, with such modifications as may be necessary to meet varying local needs and local resources.

Coming as it does as one of the series of monographs to be published under the auspices of the Committee on Medicine and the Changing Order of The New York Academy of Medicine, Dr. Mustard's contribution is most fitting and timely. Both directly and by inference he treats of many of the problems that confront the Committee, and by so doing, sheds light into many dark corners in a manner which will be of inestimable value to the Committee in its studies.

JAMES ALEXANDER MILLER, M.D.

January, 1945

THE NATURE OF THIS DOCUMENT

THE New York Academy of Medicine, on inviting the preparation of this monograph, indicated that while it did not want a history of public health in the sense of chronology, or by particularization of each advance, it did want contemporary public health work to be treated as an historical product. The letter of invitation went on further to say this: "What is wanted is not merely a survey of the present situation, but knowledge of how it came to be, perspectives to help chart the direction of future developments."

A document developed along the above lines is likely to reflect the social and political aspects of the subject rather than the scientific, and this is the case here. Further, in an attempt to present broadly the course of events in all the United States, over a period of more than a century, the discussion must be national rather than local, general rather than specific, and in terms of trends rather than of events. This will not be satisfactory to those who are preoccupied with public health organization and administrative practices of today, or who assume that the problems and routines of their respective states or localities reflect the situation in the United States as a whole.

It seems wise, too, to warn that this document is inclined to portray problems and disabilities rather than successes and strengths. Therefore, if the reader's knowledge of public health in the United States were limited to what he learned from a critical analysis of this sort, his information would be incomplete. He would fail to appreciate the fact that public health work in the United States is of a rather high order qualitatively, or that in many places the amount of service provided is comparatively satisfactory. But improvements and expansions in the future will not be attained by gloating over past accomplishments and, as this document is principally concerned with tomorrow, commendations are few and quite incidental.

There seems to be only one other matter that needs to be touched upon here. It is that any consideration of public health services operated by government must inevitably take account of certain social, economic, political, and governmental matters. These involve controversial issues which serve more often as targets of emotion than of logic. To those who do not approve of some of the social and governmental trends of today, it is suggested that it is more profitable to recognize their enemy's approach and dimensions than it is just to swear at him after being blinded by temper.

In effect, then, the sense of this document is to recognize political and social evolution as it relates to the public health, to view these things as nearly objectively as possible, to regret the passing of earlier concepts and manners, and to confess to a belief that a better public health will result from the changing order.

H.S.M.

March, 1945

ACKNOWLEDGMENTS

The author gratefully acknowledges his indebtedness to those who made it possible to include in this book the text of three historical documents bearing upon the origins of public health administration in the United States.

For suggestions that led to the discovery of the report of Alexander Hamilton to Congress in 1792, out of which arose the beginnings of the United States Public Health Service, thanks are due to Mr. Thomas P. Fleming, Assistant Director of Libraries, Columbia University, and to Mr. Seymour Robb, Librarian, College of Physicians and Surgeons, Columbia University; Mr. South Trimble, Clerk of the House of Representatives of the United States, kindly gave permission to reproduce the document, and Mr. St. George Sioussat, Chief of the Manuscript Division of the Library of Congress, was instrumental in having a photostat made.

Dr. Dwight O'Hara, Professor of Preventive Medicine, Tufts College Medical School, gave appreciated assistance in locating the order of the General Court of Massachusetts, issued in 1647 or 1648, and Mr. A. S. Salley, Secretary of the Historical Commission of South Carolina, was most courteous and helpful in locating and obtaining a photographic reproduction of the Act of the General Assembly of the Province of Carolina, 1712.

To Miss Harriet Hughes, Secretary of the School of Public Health, Columbia University, the author extends cordial thanks for her never-failing interest and cooperation in the preparation of the manuscript and particularly for assistance in compiling the bibliographical references.

H.S.M.

CONTENTS

I

CERTAIN PRELIMINARY CONSIDERATIONS

IF one studies the detailed history of an individual case of tuberculosis or heart disease, it stands out rather clearly that a multitude of factors have, or may have, entered into producing that particular illness in this particular person. As an individual, he or she has led his or her own life, has had epidemiological, psychological, sociological, and economic experiences that cannot be exactly duplicated by any other case history. And yet, if one expands tuberculosis in the individual to tuberculosis in the community, or visualizes ten thousand cases of heart disease instead of one, or otherwise views the problem of ill health in the mass, the etiology of disease falls into two principal categories: biological and sociological. Although it would oversimplify the matter to conclude that factors in either of these categories act independently of those in the other, there are certain advantages in treating them under separate headings, as in the discussion below.

Biological Factors in Health and Disease

It is difficult, of course, to consider man as but one of thousands of species, each of which is doing the best it can to strike a bargain with life. And even if it were possible to view man entirely biologically, to do so would be a mistake for his is the only species that has the power, partially at least, to adjust its environment to itself and is probably the only one that sets out deliberately to destroy other competing species. However, for the moment viewing human beings as *H. sapiens*, rather than as Man with a capital M, it becomes obvious that this species, in common with all others, has a structure and physiology geared to its particular life span. In his normal and unprotected life cycle, fluctuating to some extent because of heredity, environment, accidents, and through sheer chance, the individual of the species picks up disabilities and handicaps, pathology and degenerations. He tends to wear out, and must eventually die from something. Certainly a number of biological forces are at work here. They are operating along both general and specific lines. Thus genetic factors account for certain defects, tendencies, and accidents, and for the limiting effect of *H. sapiens'* life span. Limitation of life span, in turn, calls for an inevitable senescence and is at least partly responsible for tissue changes and degenerations. More specifically, collisions of the life cycle of *H. sapiens* with that of other species, as with *D. andersoni, T. saginatta, P. falciparum, B. typhosa,* and *C. immitis,* serve as biological hazards.

The net influence of these factors is to produce a case of illness or death, so far as concerns the individual. From the standpoint of the community or nation, they eventuate in high morbidity and mortality rates; high endemic levels in one age group from one cause, but not from another; an epidemic here or there. Pooled, these biological factors constitute one of the sources from which public health problems arise.

Sociological Factors in Health and Disease

Physicians in clinical practice are keenly aware of the manifestation of the biological forces just mentioned, and health departments, in particular, have shaped their programs largely to prevent the collision of citizens with other species. However, health departments as such have given little thought to genetic influences and have taken but little action in relation to degenerative diseases; and neither physicians working in a private capacity nor those acting for the public have paid much attention to sociological influences in relation to ill health. The exception to this is perhaps in the field of environmental sanitation, in particular relation to sewerage systems and public water supplies, and even here there is ground for suspicion that the public, for its part, has acquiesced in these facilities not so much because of a conviction of their sanitary importance as because of their convenience. It is perhaps fortunate that sanitary safety is to be found in the indoor toilet in a warm bathroom, rather than in the drafty outdoor privy.

The sociological factors that influence health and disease are as complex in their operation as are the biological ones. Further, the two overlap, sometimes aiding and abetting, sometimes offsetting one another. Thus the fact that man lives communally tends in some instances to inhibit biological factors that might contribute to disease, and to foster others that are detrimental to health. Or sociological factors may eliminate one biological hazard and substitute for it another of an entirely different nature. The tiger no longer pounces on the unwary, but the automobile does; and although life expectancy has been increased from 49 years in 1900 (1) to 64.8 in 1942 (2), this semi-biological victory means that since larger numbers of people will reach comparatively old age, a greater proportion of the population will be incapacitated with such conditions as cancer and heart disease, to which old people are peculiarly susceptible. The complexity of any organized society may, however, act on individuals in other ways, as through inadequacy or imbalance of food, through seriously detrimental housing conditions, through density of population, through noise, excitement, and the vastness of society as compared to the individual.

Society has to some extent offset its own self-generated hazards and therefore it cannot be said that the dangers of communal living are more serious at present than in jungle and tribal days. What can be said, however, is that some groups of society remain under the influence of social and biological hazards that are preventable or removable; that these groups suffer a higher rate of illness and death than those more fortunately placed; that the close relationship between sociological conditions and physical and mental disability must be recognized in any public health program.

The Character of Public Health Problems

In considering the matter of health and disease there naturally arises a question as to when a health problem becomes a public health problem. In an attempt to answer this question, a number of factors, possibly for the moment apparently irrelevant, must be recognized.

Unfortunately there is no commonly accepted definition of the phrase "public health," for the word "public" and the word "health" is each a relative term. Their principal meanings are fairly clearcut, but around their respective and specific cores both have ill-defined borders, each being qualified or influenced by the word with which it happens to be linked in any given instance. Thus, there are public schools, public lands, public utilities, public acts, public debt, public support, public spirit, public decency, public toilets. It would be difficult to define "public" in these various connections, for there is variation in the degree to which the public uses, participates in, benefits by, or is responsible for these several assets and liabilities.

A similar confusion exists as to the meaning of the word "health," in different linkages. There are found such terms as health department, health service, maternal health, child health, dental health, health education, and ill health. Again, there are two viewpoints as to health. On the one extreme are those who consider as healthy any individual who, on any given morning, is able to get out of bed and do a moderately good day's work. Such a concept of health gives no consideration to the possibility that this worker may have a progressive tuberculosis lesion, or a mild case of pellagra, or a positive Wassermann, or dermophytosis; or that in his particular instance, his domestic or occupational environment might, unless corrected, bring about in him a frank psychosis. On the other extreme, and somewhat to the left of science, are those who would consider that the status "health" is only comparative, and that there is a superlative "positive health." This school of thought appears to rely upon personal hygiene and psychology, plus health education, to produce a race with aggressive and abounding vigor, glowing with an ever present consciousness that all is well.

The concept that one is healthy if he is without fever and able to walk is in the tradition of dissecting-room medicine; the ideal that would have every man an extrovert is ultra-modern and perhaps reflects more new thought than could be substantiated medically. These extremes in points of view must be borne in mind in any discussion of public health and public health services.

To return now to the question of when a health problem becomes a public health problem. Here it may be said that the general trend is to consider that a health problem becomes a public health one when, because of its nature or extent, it may be solved only by systematized social action. The control of communicable diseases fits easily into such a concept of public health because, obviously, regulations restricting movement of those concerned can be made only by government, representing society. The provision of public water supplies or of sewerage systems is again a matter wherein there must be a pooling of social resources and, subsequently, organized community effort directed toward the building of water works and disposal systems. Other activities similarly fall easily within this broad definition of public health problems: vital statistics, health education, and other efforts where organization and large-scale administration are essential.

It is in relation to problems of the sick individual that questions arise as to the extent to which organized society, through government, should take action. One wealthy individual with diabetes, or a thousand pregnant women able to pay their way, do not necessitate any organized action for their care, and their problems would not therefore fall within the limits of the concept of a public health problem as set forth above. But a hundred diabetics uneducated as to care of their feet, unable to buy insulin or to pay a physician, or a thousand maternity cases with no funds for medical care, would necessitate organized action, whether by hospitals, by health departments, or by a privately operated clinic. The real question at issue, then, is not so much whether the person is well or ill, or even, in the last analysis, whether rich or poor—for the rich use the sewerage system—but rather when, or if, a given problem of health and disease can no longer be solved by the unassisted effort of the citizen and the uncoordinated resources of the community.

Factors that Express the Seriousness of a Public Health Problem

It is obvious that any decisions reached as to the seriousness of a given public health problem must be relative rather than absolute. But in spite of the fact that this situation is too complex for exact and sharp differentiation of values, there are certain criteria which, if applied cautiously, may serve roughly as measuring rods. These criteria may be listed, qualified, and commented upon as follows:

1. *The median annual mortality rate of the disease under consideration.* This might better be expressed as the percentage of total deaths caused by the disease in question. Other things being equal, a disease that accounts for 5 per cent of deaths from all causes is more serious than one responsible for only one tenth of one per cent of them.

2. *The median annual morbidity rate of the disease under consideration.* From a community standpoint, one would ordinarily consider the seriousness of a disease to be somewhat in proportion to the number of cases that occur each year. There

are, however, other factors that would have to be taken into consideration in this connection.

a. The case fatality: a thousand cases of dengue are not nearly so serious as a much smaller number of tetanus.

b. The length of illness: tuberculosis as against diphtheria.

c. Complications and sequelae: rheumatic fever and poliomyelitis as against chickenpox.

d. Potentialities of the disease for spread: smallpox as against pyelitis.

e. Its contribution to other conditions: syphilis in relation to stillbirths or heart disease.

3. *The age group in which the forces of mortality and morbidity express themselves.* From a biological standpoint, and even sociologically, deaths in old persons are not so serious as would be the same number of deaths in young adults. Force of mortality focused on infants and young children would entail potential rather than actual social and biological losses. However, to work out a formula that would establish relative values of life at various ages, to say for instance that one life at age 20–29 is worth ten lives at age 60–69, would involve arbitrary decisions that would vitiate results. Similar age considerations would apply to sickness, particularly in relation to wage-earning and familial responsibility.

Factors that Determine the Make-up of a Public Health Program

It seems desirable immediately to balance against the factors that express (in part) the seriousness of a public health problem those which, to a large extent, determine whether or not problems adjudged most serious are the ones to which the health department actually pays the greatest attention. Logically, between problem and control measures there should be a constant ratio: the more serious the problem, the more the health department should exert itself to combat it. This reasoning does not always apply, however, as somewhat extraneous but important practical considerations, quite apart from the seriousness of the problem, are strongly operative in shaping the pattern of public health practice. They may be listed as follows:

1. *The scientific knowledge available for prevention or control of the disease.* Failure to give due consideration to this factor is responsible for many premature conclusions that health department programs are unbalanced and not rational. But if there is meager knowledge as to how a disease may be prevented in the individual or controlled in the mass, there is little that can be done about it. On the basis of mortality rates, programs for the control of heart disease might easily be judged important enough to absorb a very large proportion of public health service. On a similar basis, activities directed toward the control of smallpox would be considered unimportant. But for control of the latter disease there is a great body of scientific knowledge; for prevention and control of the former there is comparatively little knowledge that can be applied immediately and directly.

2. *The applicability of scientific knowledge.* Even though it might be known how to prevent a given disease, or to reduce its high endemic level, or to eliminate it as an epidemic, it may be impracticable to apply the knowledge. Some of the factors that interfere with utilizing available knowledge are these:

a. The problem may be so disseminated and masked as to make discovery of foci impossible: mild cases of influenza, not incapacitated, not under medical care; ticks infected with the rickettsia; interstate travel of a person with gonorrhea.

b. Control might involve procedures that would infringe upon the legal rights of individuals: the right to carry a cold to work, to drink to excess if the peace is not disturbed; the right to discreet fornication; the right to call in a faith-healer for the cure of diphtheria.

c. An unfavorable attitude on the part of the public, either indifference or opposition, may in some instances make application of a measure impossible. Thus religious convictions against vaccination might offset community-wide procedures along these lines. Similarly, activities that produce no tangible results, or which may accomplish something only in the future, get little public support.

d. The attitude of the medical profession or its spokesmen may slow up the application of knowledge by the health department. This inhibiting factor arises, as a rule, only when the program concerned is regarded by medical organizations or individuals as leading toward government interference or regimentation.

e. The cost of an undertaking may make it impossible to apply knowledge. In some states, a want of beds for tuberculosis has made the program of the health department largely ineffective in this activity.

3. *Legal requirements.* It must never be forgotten that a public health program may be, and is, shaped to a considerable degree by Acts of Congress, by state legislatures, and in many places by city ordinances. Forces of this sort operate strongly both positively and negatively. A local, state, or federal health program might by old statutes be forced to continue activities currently recognized as unnecessary or ineffective; or be emasculated, revitalized, or extended into new fields by current legislation.

Aesthetics and Public Health

Differentiation between aesthetic and hygienic measures is of considerable importance in public health work, particularly in local activities. Perhaps one of the first to make this distinction was John Snow, an Englishman who, astonishingly, combined a very high degree of efficiency in two quite unrelated medical activities: anesthesia and epidemiology. In the latter field he demonstrated (1849–1854) the role of water in cholera, and in 1855 he entered into a brisk argument with the General Board of Health of London on the matter of nuisances. His views, as expressed by his biographer, Richardson, are unusually clear and succinct.

No mere emanation arising from evolution of foul smelling gases can, *per se*, according to his views, originate a specific disease, such as smallpox or scarlet fever; as well expect that the evolution of such gases should plant a plain with oaks or a garden with crocuses. The smallpox may occur over a cesspool as an oak may spring up through a manure heap; but the smallpox would never appear over the cesspool in the absence of its specific poison; nor the oak rise from the manure heap in the absence of the acorn which seeded it. . . . He indicated . . . that he was no defender of nuisances, but that whereas a bad smell cannot, simply because it is a bad smell, give rise to specific disease, so an offensive business conducted in a place where it ought not be, should be proceeded against by ordinary law as a nuisance, without applying to it the word pestiferous, or otherwise dragging in and distorting the science of medicine (3).

The last clause of the above quotation is significant enough to repeat: "Dragging in and distorting the science of medicine." It is a danger that continues to exist and to the detriment of real advances. City councils, even today, may resist providing adequate hospital care for the tuberculous, for instance, but for purposes of widening a sidewalk will, with piety, invoke the old expression "the public health demanding it." Similarly, individuals with little scientific information but urged by a great enthusiasm still lay down schedules of personal hygiene, commendable enough as decent things to do but not the panaceas that their proponents declare them to be.

Relationships between Official and Voluntary Health Agencies

It requires only casual study of the situation to learn that a great deal of work, important in maintaining public health, is done outside of official governmental agencies. Valuable contributions are made by voluntary organizations, supported by private funds and in no way connected with the government. A detailed description of these agencies would carry this discussion far afield, but it does seem pertinent to consider here the relationship of voluntary health organizations to those of government.

Viewing the matter from the standpoint of health departments, it may be said that voluntary organizations have rendered valuable aid through their ability to explore fields closed to the official agencies because of lack of funds. In an official agency the public health administrator must be able to promise, or at least to infer to his appropriating body, that the investment of public funds will yield fairly quick and substantial returns. In contrast with this, the governing board of a voluntary agency is quite prepared, and has authority, to pioneer in new public health territory. In many instances, therefore, the program of the health department lags somewhat behind that of a voluntary agency in one special line or another. After the voluntary agency has demonstrated that a given undertaking is productive, the health department moves forward into the area of endeavor and the voluntary agency again advances to new frontiers.

The voluntary agency has also contributed to the establishment of high standards of performance. In many special fields it has been able to obtain the advice and interested cooperation of highly competent authorities and has insisted upon standards of performance which might not have evolved through the routine work of health departments.

A third contribution, somewhat intangible but nevertheless important, is in the field of public health education. The voluntary agencies have served skilfully in obtaining public understanding and support of health work. They have on their governing boards, as a rule, citizens prominent locally and even nationally, and these, being strategically placed, have been able to influence the enactment of sound public health laws and provisions.

What has been said above represents the optimistic or idealistic aspect of the relationship between health departments and voluntary agencies. There is, however, another side to it. Sometimes it happens that the voluntary agency serves as a deterrent to the establishment or the expansion of a health department, particularly a local one, in that there is occasionally an inclination on the part of voluntary workers to regard the community or the special field in which they operate as their vested interest. They tend to lose sight of the fact that their function is essentially to explore, pilot, and supplement, and are loath to relinquish to the health department the services that they have worked so hard to build. This reluctance is rationalized by the claim that the health department is not really competent to take over the activity, or that politics will enter into it, or that it is not a field in which government should or might successfully operate. These are in some instances very good and substantial reasons but more often they are excuses and the real reason is likely to be found in the vested interest concept mentioned above.

Professions that Participate in Public Health Work

As previously indicated, the term public health is an elastic one, shaped by many circumstances. Further, it is important to have clearly in mind that many activities not considered as public health work contribute tremendously to the health of the public: thus research work, medical and nursing education, the work of hospital and social agencies, the improvement of economic and living conditions, the elimination of illiteracy, and the achievement of a higher educational level. From the preceding list there has been purposely omitted a group that makes a vast contribution. It has been left out in order to have it stand by itself: the physician in private practice. It is he who cares for the greater portion of the sick, and although the illnesses of those whom he attends might in many instances have been prevented, the fact remains that these preventive measures were not applied. Since these people are sick, the physician's part in returning them to health and productivity is a social contribution of no small importance, though not always recognized by those who are preoccupied in their ever upward straining.

Not only is the physician of importance because of his care of the sick but, when all is said and done, it is around him, representing medical science, that public health programs must be built. Thus, although in a few places the health officer is a layman, it is generally agreed that the health officer should have a medical background. Occasionally quite large health departments have lay administrators at their head, but more generally the lay health officer is found in the township.

There are those who maintain that in large organizations the necessity for administrative competence outweighs the requirements for medical knowledge and that lay direction is really preferable to medical. At the opposite extreme are those who, possibly somewhat over-conscious of themselves as physicians, look askance at the participation in public health programs of anyone who has not the degree of a doctor of medicine. Perhaps it is sensible to believe that in very large health organizations the virtues and the deficiencies of the lay and medical person would to some extent offset one another. Other things being equal, each would have his strengths and weaknesses. In smaller health departments, however, this can never be the case, for the health officer must himself be prepared to deal with physicians and to participate in all the various aspects of the program. To do these things he must possess sound medical knowledge. The lay person, therefore, cannot function in this capacity and is out of place as the head of the average health department; when he attempts to hold the office, he must limit his activities to sanitation, to health education, and in general to a sort of administrative clerkship.

The above discussion is related essentially to the top position in the health department. Naturally, there are many important positions other than that of chief, and these positions are filled by individuals trained in a number of professions: medicine, engineering, nursing, dentistry, bacteriology, veterinary medicine, chemistry, and others.

Engineers, nurses, bacteriologists, and other specialists who serve the health department usually devote their full time to the work. This is not always the case with physicians and dentists and veterinarians, and an important question in public health administration is the extent to which part-time professional personnel can and should be utilized by the health department.

In many instances this question is answered in favor of the part-time service for no reason other than that there is too little money available to permit the employment of a full-time person. In the case of physicians, which will serve to illustrate the general policy followed, positions involving administrative as well as technical duties are likely to be filled by full-time personnel. In positions that require mainly professional competence, as service in a tuberculosis clinic or in a well-child conference, part-time physicians may often be used advantageously. The disadvantage of the part-time physician is that he may be inclined to think only in terms of individuals cared for, remain oblivious of the influence of the home environment of individuals served, and exhibit little interest or competence in the operation and administration of the clinic as a community facility.

This whole matter of the coordination of the work of physicians in practice with that of the health department and the relationship involved may of course come into sharp focus if or when a fairly far-reaching medical care program operated by government is instituted. There can be no question but that the physician who regularly sees cases of illness or near-illness, who enters many homes each day, who conducts periodic examinations, has a better opportunity than anyone else to contribute to the health of the whole family and through the family to that of the community. However, it must be confessed that the physician in private practice has not in the past functioned completely in this capacity. He has seen his patients as sick persons and has been inclined to limit his interest in a given family to the particular person whom he has been called to attend. Perhaps ethics have restricted him and have caused him to feel that persistent inquiry as to the health of other members of the patient's family might cause them to think that he is attempting to drum up new business; perhaps too, and more likely, he has been under such pressure to take care of the sick for whom he is responsible that he has been preoccupied with this to the exclusion of opportunities to serve as an active continuing health counselor for the family. But regardless of the past and the reasons for it, there can be no doubt that the health of the public would be substantially improved if physicians, who see sick people day in and day out, had the time and the interest to function for the whole family, sick, ailing, and well. As it is today, the public health nurse has in effect taken over this potentiality of medical practice (4).

Education for Public Health Work

One may become proficient in public health work only by trial and error. The process may be shortened, and the proportion of errors reduced, by graduate study, but one cannot become a competent health officer, for instance, without having served as one.

It is more and more the custom at present, for those who are qualified in a profession basic to public health, to pursue postgraduate study in the latter field. A number of the larger universities in the United States provide courses designed to serve in this connection. The curriculum ordinarily provides basic and advanced instruction in public health organization and administration, epidemiology, biostatistics, sanitation, health education, plus a choice of electives in special fields. A master's degree in public health is offered to those who complete satisfactorily one year of work. The degree of doctor of public health is limited to those of unusual competence who may wish to pursue further study and investigation. There is an inclination to confer this degree only on those already qualified as doctors of medicine.

As a rule, physicians, dentists, engineers pursue the same course for about one half of the year, that is, to completion of subjects fundamental to a public health career. For the remainder of the year, students follow those electives which fit into their respective professional backgrounds. Instruction for public health nurses is more frequently provided through teachers' colleges than through public health schools.

The American Public Health Association publishes annually a statement as to the number of persons in the several professional categories who receive graduate degrees (5). These data are further broken down by kind of degrees and by universities. The special technical group concerned with graduate education in public health is the Association of Public Health Schools. The following universities have membership in this association: Columbia, Harvard, Johns Hopkins, Michigan, Minnesota, North Carolina, Vanderbilt, Yale, and Toronto in Canada.

Particularly pertinent to this discussion is that health departments are more and more demanding that candidates for appointments possess among other qualifications a graduate degree in public health. This directly contributes to staff competence, and indirectly blocks the politician's importunities that this or that unqualified person be given consideration for a position in the health department. Pending a greater reserve of well-trained workers, health agencies offer fellowships to young physicians, nurses, engineers, dentists, whom they employ at the end of a period of study. The Federal Government has recognized the need for such fellowships, and has authorized the use of state-aid funds for this purpose. Supplementary to formal basic university training in public health, and of just about equal importance, programs of in-service training are offered to staff members by all well-organized health departments.

An important preliminary to graduate public health study or to the practice of medicine is the kind of instruction that physicians receive in preventive medicine and public health in medical schools. Viewing the matter from the standpoint of the medical student, one may say that he is much less likely to adopt a career in public health than in some clinical phase of medicine, which is as it should be. But with the changes that appear likely to come about in medical practice, it seems that a knowledge of preventive medicine and public health will become of increasing importance to all physicians of the future. The character of instruction in this field has improved in recent years, and there is a new interest in it. Both the American Public Health Association and the Association of American Medical Colleges have designated committees to study the matter, and the report of the latter organization was recently published (6).

Government in Its Relation to Public Health Work

The fact that there are three areas or strata of government in the United States is confusing to visitors from other countries, and to not a few native sons. But if one is to understand the development of health departments in the United States, their current positions, and their interrelationships, then the limitations and extent of local, state, and Federal Government must be known and kept in mind.

The original thirteen states were sovereign powers before the

Constitution of the United States was adopted. Thus, the states did not have authority conferred on them by an already established central government, but quite the reverse: the states established that government and ceded to it certain powers and responsibilities. In this arrangement, two principles stood out: 1) in those fields in which the Federal Government was given authority, its laws would take precedence over state laws should the two be in conflict; 2) those powers not ceded to the Federal Government would remain with the states. In the circumstances one may not, correctly, visualize the Federal Government as possessing greater power than an individual state government. The situation is rather that the state government, on the one hand, and the Federal Government, on the other, occupy different areas of responsibility and authority. But in spite of this theoretical and in most cases actual differentiation of inherent powers, the above statement tends somewhat to oversimplify the matter, in that with the passage of time there has been a tendency to give a widely inclusive interpretation to just what the states ceded to the Federal Government under the Constitution. Correspondingly, there has been a shrinkage in the dimensions of that area which the states thought they were reserving to themselves.

The trend toward a stronger Federal Government has been present, of course, ever since the establishment of that government, and has been furthered and utilized, or opposed and viewed with apprehension, in accordance with the political philosophy of individuals in succeeding generations. Public health undertakings of government inevitably are affected by the net outcome of these influences in Congresses, state legislatures, city councils, and boards of health, for the program of a health department must develop within the framework of the government of which it forms a part. At the moment, the pace toward a stronger Federal Government has been greatly accelerated. Not only that, but large units of government tend in general to press upon smaller ones, to help them, to guide them, to give them money, to anesthetize them, to circumscribe their respective local autonomies. This is reflected in public health work, for the federal agencies press on state health departments, and the latter, in turn, become more and more paternalistic toward local health departments.

The rightness or wrongness of this matter is not the question here at issue. So far as it concerns public health work, two things are significant. The first is that the trend exists and, regardless of what one thinks was the original intent of those referred to as the Founding Fathers, health departments must work under and with this situation. The second consideration, and again this is for those who are on the states-rights rather than the federalist side, is that public health work has improved greatly in scope and character as a result of federal participation; nor is there much hope that each community in the nation can ensure health service to its citizens without strong, perhaps increased, federal and state assistance.

The authority of the Federal Government to carry on public health work is derived rather than direct. There is no reference to health in the Constitution and it is therefore necessary that federal legislation in this field be oblique, resting upon well-defined authority in some other field. This approach will be illustrated subsequently; for the moment it may be said that the parts of the Constitution of the United States upon which federal health legislation is based are the following:

Article I, Section VIII, Paragraph I. [The Congress shall have power]

To lay and collect taxes, duties, imposts, and excises, to pay the debts and provide for the common defense and general welfare of the United States; but all duties, imposts, and excises shall be uniform throughout the United States;

Article I, Section VIII, Paragraph III. [The Congress shall have power]
To regulate commerce with foreign nations and among the several States, and with the Indian tribes;

Article I, Section VIII, Paragraph XVII. [The Congress shall have power]
To exercise exclusive legislation in all cases whatsoever over such district (not exceeding ten miles square) as may, by cession of particular States and the acceptance of Congress, become the seat of the Government of the United States, and to exercise like authority over all places purchased by the consent of the legislature of the State in which the same shall be, for the erection of forts, magazines, arsenals, dockyards, and other needful buildings; and

Article II, Section II, Paragraph II. [Powers of the President]
He shall have power, by and with the advice and consent of the Senate, to make treaties, provided two thirds of the Senators present concur . . .

Utilization of the several clauses contained in the above paragraphs, in relation to public health, has been such that the enforcement elements in federal legislation are derived from those clauses dealing with commerce, treaties, and taxes. Legislation involving investigation of disease and state aid is based on the implications of "general welfare."

The authority of states to engage in public health work derives from two principal sources: police power, inherent in all sovereign bodies; and the Tenth Amendment to the Constitution, which says that "the powers not granted to the United States by the Constitution nor prohibited to it by the states, are reserved to the states respectively, or to the people." This of course is a negative sort of thing from the standpoint of the states, and its intent has been subject to various interpretations not directly relevant to this discussion. A few state constitutions make reference to the public health, but not many. The vast authority of police power is the general basis upon which responsibility for state and local health programs rests.

Assuming, then, that all areas of government have sound constitutional authority for engaging in health work in their respective spheres, this preliminary consideration of the matter may be closed by the re-statement of the obvious: the activation of constitutional authority and the delivery of health service are brought about by acts of legislative bodies, regulations of boards of health or their counterparts, and executive interpretations and directives.

The preceding discussion of somewhat diverse matters is designed to serve as a background for the concept that public health service at any given time and place represents, in a way, the confluence of two streams in human progress. First, there is the fairly clear and clean, but somewhat cold, trickle that filters down through the very fine sands of science; and second, there is the somewhat muddy flow of varying temperature that gushes intermittently from the rich but unpatrolled socio-political pastures. Taking their rise as they do in such entirely different sources, it is not astonishing that these tributaries do not completely or smoothly mix on their conjunction; nor need one be discouraged because there are eddies and backwashes, flotsam and froth. It is a powerful stream, and one that will continue to flow. Stream control, in this instance, becomes a function of public health administration, and the chapters that follow constitute an attempt to explore headwaters, in the belief that a knowledge of watersheds and terrain may contribute to control measures.

REFERENCES

1. Fisher, Irving. Lengthening of Human Life in Retrospect and Prospect. American Journal of Public Health, 17:1, January 1927.

2. Metropolitan Life Insurance Company. Statistical Bulletin, 25:4, April 1944.
3. Snow, John. Snow on Cholera: A Reprint of Two Papers Together with a Biographical Memoir by B. W. Richardson and an Introduction by Wade Hampton Frost. New York: The Commonwealth Fund, 1936, p. xxxix.
4. For a discussion of the family as the unit of illness and the unit of treatment by the physician, see Richardson, Henry B. Patients Have Families. New York: The Commonwealth Fund, 1945.
5. American Public Health Association, Committee on Professional Education. Public Health Degrees and Certificates Granted in the United States and Canada. Published annually for each academic year. The last statement will be found in the American Journal of Public Health, 34:1264, December 1944.

   This Association's Committee on Professional Education has also published, to November 1944, reports on educational qualifications for public health workers, as follows: Public Health Engineers, Sanitarians, Sub-Professional Field Personnel in Sanitation, Public Health Statisticians, Health Officers, Nutritionists in Health Agencies, Industrial Hygienists, Public Health Nurses in Industry, Public Health Nursing Personnel, Public Health Laboratory Workers, Health Educators.
6. Association of American Medical Colleges. Report of the Committee on Teaching of Public Health and Preventive Medicine. Journal of the Association of American Medical Colleges, 20:161, May 1945.

FEDERAL HEALTH SERVICES

FEDERAL health work in the United States is not established as a coordinated unit. On the contrary, sub-units are scattered throughout the several departments and bureaus of the Government, and there are unwise separations and unnecessary overlapping of functions. Not by the greatest stretch of the imagination and sympathetic understanding can it be said that the situation is as it should be. It violates design; it is diffuse; it inhibits coordinated action and invites confusion. And yet, amazingly enough, the individual federal health services function quite efficiently in their respective spheres; and if there is no order in the existing arrangement, there are at least explanations for it.

Whether or not future pressures will result in a better coordination of the Federal Government's health activities or will tip the balance toward a situation where existing parts become greater and the whole remains non-existent, must remain to some extent an open question. But if the latter contingency is to be avoided and a better balance and order are to be attained, those influences that have brought about the present arrangement must as nearly as possible be discovered and analyzed. And too, within the limits of practicability, it must be determined to what extent these old pressures, interests, and excitants persist in the present and are likely to operate in the future.

As a point of departure in such a consideration, today's public health activities of the Federal Government may be outlined by the following flat, and for the moment unqualified, statements:

1. The principal health agency of the Federal Government is the United States Public Health Service. This forms a part of the Federal Security Agency.

2. About forty other federal agencies participate to some degree in public health or medical care activities. The public health and medical programs of most of these agencies are limited, but in a few instances exceedingly important activities are pursued quite independently of the principal agency.

3. Those federal agencies which, in addition to the Public Health Service, operate in important areas of the health field include the following:

Department of Agriculture. The Bureaus of Animal Industry, Home Economics, Dairy Industry, Entomology and Plant Quarantine.

Department of Commerce. Division of Vital Statistics, Bureau of the Census.

Department of the Interior. Office of Indian Affairs, in sanitation and medical care; Division of Territories and Island Possessions, in some aspects of its activities; Bureau of Mines, in industrial hygiene.

Federal Security Agency. Pure Food and Drug Administration, formerly in the Department of Agriculture; Office of Education, formerly in the Department of the Interior.

Department of Labor. Division of Maternal and Child Health, Children's Bureau; Bureau of Labor Statistics.

These are the principal federal agencies that engage in public health and medical care. Others have limited and highly specialized programs. Thus federal participation in public health and medical work may be said to vary from the nurse-attended rest room to the widespread activities of the United States Public Health Service. As many of them represent no more than an attempt to provide a day-bed for those with cramps, it would be unproductive to attempt to trace the beginnings and developments of all such federal activities. The evolutions of some, however, are of significance and indicate how in one way or another, under various pressures, urges, and interests, federal health services came into existence and grew.

Of most significance are the origins and evolution of the United States Public Health Service. Even here it is impracticable and not entirely desirable to follow all historical aspects, but it does seem advisable to provide enough detail to indicate how public health problems came to attention, the administrative measures adopted for their solution, mistakes made and advances scored, and to determine whether or not certain precedents and trends, developed a century ago, are likely to continue. In describing the development of the United States Public Health Service, particular attention will be directed to the evolution of its programs in medical care, foreign quarantine, interstate quarantine, and states' relations. Federal health activities conducted by other national agencies such as those relating to maternal and child hygiene, vital statistics, food and drug control, need be considered only to the extent that their past and present statuses give what seems an insight into possible trends in the future.

UNITED STATES PUBLIC HEALTH SERVICE

A consideration of the Federal Government's principal health agency may well be introduced by an examination of its official seal. This sets forth significant facts as to the origin and development of federal health work; it may imply future developments. The seal consists of a fouled anchor on which is crossed a caduceus, with the date 1798 inscribed below. That the caduceus refers to the healing art is obvious; the fouled anchor represents the sailor in distress, and the date indicates the year of enactment of the first federal law relating to medical care of merchant seamen. Around the perimeter is lettered "U. S. Public Health Service."

Although 1798 is generally accepted as the birth date of what is now the United States Public Health Service, one must go even further back than this for its inception. Actually this venture of the newly formed national government came about under the stimulation of that somewhat austere federalist, Alexander Hamilton. It would appear that to him, as Secretary of the Treasury in 1792, had come "certain papers concerning a marine Hospital at the town of Washington, in the State of Virginia [near Norfolk], and a memorial of the Marine Society of Boston." His action was to prepare a report which he transmitted to Congress on April 16, 1792. Inasmuch as this is of considerable importance historically and so far as is known has not before been made available in any publication, the first page of the document is reproduced here; the complete text will be found in the Appendix.

A Federal Venture in Medical Care

Nearly six years after Hamilton's recommendations, on Wednesday, February 28, 1798, to be exact, Mr. Livingston (New York), from the Committee of Commerce and Manufacture, reported in the House of Representatives of the United States a bill "for the relief of sick and disabled Seamen." This bill set forth that such relief was to be financed by the deduction of twenty cents per month from each seaman's wages; that the President might appoint directors of Marine Hospitals in the several ports of the United States; that it would be their duty to arrange for hospitalization and provide care of this particular group of individuals; and that Marine Hospitals might be built. No salary was provided for the directors but they were to be reimbursed for necessary expenditures incurred. Moneys collected were to be kept for use in the district in which they were obtained. Each director designated was responsible to the local Collector of Customs who, in turn, represented the President of the United States. The bill was approved July 16, 1798 (2).

Viewing this Act from the perspective of 1941, and expressing its various provisions in modern phraseology, Falk has the following to say:

The Secretary of the Treasury, to whom were referred certain papers concerning a marine Hospital at the town of Washington in the State of Virginia, and a memorial of the Marine Society of Boston, on the subject of marine Hospitals, respectfully submits the following Report:

The establishment of one or more marine Hospitals in the United States is a measure desirable on various accounts. The interests of humanity are concerned in it, from its tendency to protect from want and misery, a very useful, and, for the most part, a very needy class of the Community. The interests of navigation and trade are also concerned in it, from the protection and relief which it is calculated to afford to the same class; conducing to attract and attach seamen to the country.

A fund for the purpose may, it is presumed, be most conveniently derived from the expedient suggested in the above-mentioned Memorial, namely, a contribution by the mariners and seamen of the United States, out of their wages to be regulated by law.

The rate of the contribution may be two cents per month for each mariner or seaman, to be reserved, pursuant to articles, by masters of vessels, and paid to the collectors of districts, to which the vessels respectively belong. Effectual regulations for this purpose may, without difficulty, be devised.

The benefit of the fund ought to extend, not only to
disabled

FIRST STEP IN THE ESTABLISHMENT OF THE UNITED STATES
PUBLIC HEALTH SERVICE

Report transmitted to Congress by Alexander Hamilton, April 17, 1792

This oldest medical service is significant in three respects: 1) it was established for self-supporting, not dependent persons— Americans, seamen and the personnel of the Navy; 2) it was financed by a tax on seamen, by payroll deductions from the pay of officers, seamen, and marines in the Navy, and by general taxation; and 3) it included treatment by private physicians and hospital care. As long ago, then, as 1798–99, the principle was accepted that the Federal Government should provide tax-supported medical services and hospitalization for certain classes of independent (non-relief) persons under what was one of the first systems of compulsory sickness insurance in the world (3).

Similarly, Terris hails this Act as "An Early System of Compulsory Health Insurance in the United States" (4). Such tight cataloguing and crisp views, in which today's concepts and objectives are attributed to those who acted nearly a century and a half ago, have within them the same danger that exists in other brisk and modern interpretations of events long passed: one may read into them a wanted meaning. As a fact accomplished, this Act of 1798 was in the nature of insurance, and it was compulsory. But in light of the problems, thoughts, and attitudes then current, it would appear questionable to attribute to the Fifth Congress, in admiration or condemnation, an intent to institute a medical insurance scheme as such schemes are today regarded. In the circumstances, it would seem wise to go back to the record and attempt to determine what Congress thought it was doing when it enacted this legislation.

When this bill was introduced, John Adams was President and this was the Fifth Congress of the United States. George Washington and many others who had participated in framing the Constitution only about a decade before were still alive; some of them were in Congress. Tentatively and somewhat fearsomely the newly formed Federal Government was feeling its way toward nationalism. The word State, even when used in the abstract, was capitalized; and legislators said "The United States are," or "The United States have," rather than "The United States is," or "The United States has." It was, therefore, in an atmosphere surcharged with the consciousness of state sovereignty, on the one hand, and of suspicion of the newly formed government of the United States, on the other, and strongly influenced by contending sectional interests, that Mr. Livingston's bill was introduced and discussed. The records of discussion are none too complete, but it would appear that the principal proponents of the bill were Mr. Livingston of New York, Mr. Pinckney of South Carolina, and Mr. Parker of Virginia. The principal opposition was furnished by representatives from Massachusetts, and by Mr. Gallatin from Pennsylvania.

This merchant seamen's bill came on the calendar of the House for final discussion on April 10, 1798, and Mr. Sewall of Massachusetts took the floor. He said* that he objected to this bill because in the part of the Union from whence he came, provision is already made for sick and disabled persons of every description, sailors as well as others, with which every person in the community is charged. Seamen in that quarter, therefore, now pay their full proportion of money for public charity. He doubted the propriety of taxing seamen only for the support of what ought to be considered as a public charity. He thought the laws of reason and charity called upon the public at large in support of unfortunate men of this description, and that the burden ought not exclusively to be laid upon them. He objected to the bill further because it considered these men (sailors) as incapable of taking care of themselves, and because it calls upon them to subscribe for their own support in case of sickness or inability without taking a farthing from the pocket of the United States or of the gentleman himself (Mr. Livingston).

---

* From here through page 31 the phraseology used is as it appears in the Annals of Congress, except that occasional introductory clauses are interpolated (5).

Mr. Varnum of Massachusetts said he did not know but that the United States have the power to make the proposed regulation, but he thought it was a business which more particularly concerned the Legislatures of the individual States. If the United States, indeed, thought this class of men of so much more importance than any other, the people at large, he thought, ought to support them in distress and if hospitals are to be supported for this purpose, the public ought to support them and not the sailors themselves. He did not think that the kind of tax proposed in the bill was consistent with federal principles. He did not see how it could be reconciled with that clause of the Constitution which says that no capitation, or other direct tax, shall be laid unless in proportion to the census or enumeration directed to be taken.* For it might as well be said, continued Mr. Varnum, that because the State of Massachusetts is possessed of some particular advantage over other States, every citizen of that State shall pay a poll tax of $10 a year for the benefit of the Union, as that the sailors of that State should be called upon to support an establishment in which they will be little interested.

Mr. Gallatin said that this bill assumed a principle for its foundation, the truth of which he was not acquainted with, viz.: that the seamen of the United States are not able to provide for themselves, and, therefore, that it is necessary to provide a sum for their relief, in case of sickness or disability. He had not seen this distinction between them and other classes of citizens, and, therefore, believed them to be capable of taking care of themselves. He knew there were, in all communities, a number of men who were not sufficiently provident to lay by money to afford relief in sickness, or to make old age comfortable; but he did not know that there was a greater number of this description of persons among seamen than

* It will be remembered that the first federal income tax efforts ran afoul this same clause. The difficulty was resolved by the Sixteenth Amendment.

among others. He thought it better to leave the business as at present, and suffer this class of people to provide for themselves, or to be provided for in the same way in which other poor and sick or disabled persons are supported.

He was opposed also to the manner in which the fund is proposed to be raised. If he was inclined to provide relief for sailors, as a distinct class of citizens, he was against providing a fund for the purpose by a tax upon labor, which would, in all respects, be a capitation tax. Gentlemen might argue as they pleased about the tax falling upon merchants, it was impossible to say upon whom a tax upon labor would fall. In some instances it would fall upon the sailors themselves; and in some of these it would be paid by the merchants themselves, and in others, by the community.

Mr. J. Parker, of Virginia, spoke rather briefly in support of the bill, asking, when the country is threatened with war, what encouragement was there for men to enter on board our vessels, if there were no asylum for them in case they were sick or wounded. It would be wise and politic, in his opinion, to begin measures which must place these persons in a better situation than at present. He cited the Greenwich Hospital for British sailors and urged similar provisions by the United States.

Mr. Pinckney of South Carolina was sorry to differ from his friend from Massachusetts on this subject. He had hoped the objections which he had before stated to the principle of this bill would, by this time, have been removed. The gentleman had before stated, that his principal objection to this bill arose from there being already provision made in the Eastern States for the relief of sick and disabled seamen. It was then stated in reply, that provided the law did bear a little hard upon that State, from their known federal disposition, it was hoped, as it would operate a general benefit to the Union, it would not be objected to. But it was then shown, and he would repeat it, that the law could not bear

hard upon them. If there is a provision at present made in Massachusetts for persons of this description, it must be a burden upon
the people there; and if, after the passing of this law, that burden
be removed, it would certainly be beneficial to the citizens of that
State in general, though it may be a tax upon the seamen.

The gentleman from Massachusetts had also spoken against the
general utility of the measure. He said it was taxing a particular
description of men for a general object. On the contrary, he thought
it only reasonable and equitable that these persons should pay for
the benefit which they were themselves to receive, and that it
would be neither just nor fair for other persons to pay it. But he
believed if the subject was further looked into it would be found
that the seamen would not pay the tax themselves, as it would
come to be considered as wages, and by that means become a general tax, as the merchant who would have to pay it would lay it
upon his merchandise.

Mr. Livingston's arguments were not very forceful. One suspects
that there had been considerable previous committee argument
about this bill, and that its proponent, knowing it would pass, discussed it in this instance rather as a matter of form. Actually, Mr.
Livingston, in dealing with his opponents, said that notwithstand-
ing the pertinacious opposition that this bill has received from the
gentleman last up (Mr. Sewall) he doubted not it would pass by a
large majority. If he knew anything of the careless, honest nature
of this class of men, they would not object to so trifling a sum as
twenty cents a month for so valuable an object. A sailor, said he, is
concerned only for the present, and is incapable of thinking of, or
inattentive to, future welfare; he is, therefore, a proper object for
the care of Government, and whilst he can provide an asylum for
infirmity or old age, by the sacrifices of a few gills of rum, he will
not scruple to do it.

In this somewhat paraphrased account of the Congressional discussion relating to the bill for relief of seamen, and in view of the final action taken, there are recorded certain attitudes and events which were to be of significance in federal-state relationships and which were to serve as guides to the Federal Government in its public health and medical activities for the next century and a quarter. Their influence is felt today and may shape future trends. In this connection, the following would seem worth consideration:

1. This bill on its introduction was referred to the "Committee on Commerce and Manufacture." No one appears to have considered the possibility that there might be established a committee on public health or on medical care. *The health or medical care element* came under consideration only because it was a problem of commerce. Thus to regard medical and health matters as secondary and to approach them indirectly has, until recently, been the practice in the Congress of the United States, and to no small extent accounts for the wide scattering of federal health activities among the various departments.

2. Hamilton visualized care of seamen as a measure desirable in the interests of humanity, "to protect from want and misery, a very useful, and, for the most part, a very needy Class of the Community." He mentioned also the interests of "navigation and trade," and felt that the measure might "attract and attach seamen to the country." Parker, of Virginia, hoped that the Act might make it less difficult to get seamen "to enter on board our vessels." Thus was strongly emphasized the national interest in commerce.

3. This Act for the relief of sick and disabled seamen was not planned as a progressive move that would give merchant seamen something better than the average citizen received in the way of medical care. Actually, it was an effort to remove from merchant seamen, as sort of federal step-wards, a handicap under which not even paupers suffered: paupers could obtain such medical care as was available for them in their respective home communities in the several states. Seamen were not eligible for even this meager care if sick or disabled away from their home

port, as they were not, in the local sense, citizens. A modern version of this problem is seen when the migratory worker requires hospitalization because of tuberculosis.

4. In the discussion of the bill, serious questions as to the legality of the procedure were raised:

a. Double taxation: supposedly, seamen already paid their local taxes for support of charity, and this would constitute a second tax.

b. Unconstitutionality: it would be a federal tax on a basis other than population.

c. State responsibility: the matter was one which might more properly be considered by the respective state legislatures than by the Federal Congress.

5. It was not proposed nor was it prohibited that the Federal Government develop its own medical care program. Early arrangements, however, suggest that it was originally visualized as a program to be operated indirectly through local contracts for medical and hospital service. Hospitals could be built, but even when built by federal funds, might be operated through local contracts.

6. It was locally autonomous and not a national system.

When the Act of 1798 became effective July 16 of that year, it related only to merchant seamen. It is perhaps significant of the tendency of federal services to grow that in the following year the Act was amended to provide similar benefits, on a likewise required payment of twenty cents a month, to each sailor and officer of the Navy, including the marines. It was further amended so that the old prohibition against using funds collected in one port for relief of beneficiaries in another was lifted to the extent that money collected in ports of one state could be applied in an adjoining state. Here was an effort to spread resources, to pool risks; a move toward nationalization. This effort met with opposition, but not, apparently, because of any expressed objection to nationalization of the fund. The objection seems rather to have been in the nature

of conflicting sectional interests. Massachusetts, with great maritime commerce, could not, with equanimity, see funds collected
locally go into a pool for the benefit of sailors in those ports which
did not collect so much money. The compromise arranged was
that an exception be made in the case of Massachusetts, and its
contiguous states: Rhode Island, Connecticut, New Hampshire.
Money collected in any one of them could be expended only in that
state. This exception continued in force until 1802 when all funds
were pooled for the common purpose of providing relief to the
beneficiaries.

Here, then, was an arrangement for medical and hospital service
through the utilization of local facilities, rather than for direct service by medical officers employed by the Federal Government.
There was, however, the provision that marine hospitals might be
built should no local facilities exist. But even here, direct operation
by the Federal Government was not apparently visualized. How
this nucleus of medical care grew to the present Bureau of Medical Service of the United States Public Health Service and, in fact,
into the Public Health Service itself, ought to contain some lessons
for the future, if the facts can be discovered.

Only fragmentary and incomplete records of developments were
kept during the first seventy-five years of the Act for the relief of
merchant seamen. Such data as have survived are contained in reports of the Secretary of the Treasury, and in collateral documents
arising from sources other than the relief of seamen program. Perhaps the clearest obtainable picture of events from 1798 to 1870 is
to be found in the *First Annual Report of the Marine Hospital
Service of the United States,* prepared by Dr. John M. Woodworth,
the Service's first Supervising Surgeon, and published in 1872 (6).

Dr. Woodworth's first and subsequent reports, and other documents, indicate that in the beginning things did not go well with
this government venture. Various arrangements were made for

medical and hospital care, and complaints and criticisms arose. The indirect methods of providing medical care and of building and operating hospitals may be illustrated by Dr. Woodworth's account of the Charleston, South Carolina, undertaking, as follows:

The hospital at Charleston, South Carolina, referred to by the Secretary of the Treasury in 1802, appears not to have been a government hospital, as a marine hospital at that port was first opened to receive seamen in the year 1834. In June, 1802, Mr. Gallatin, then Secretary of the Treasury, proposed to the City Council of Charleston that they should take charge of such sick and disabled seamen as might apply for relief at that place, for which they were to receive the hospital dues collected at their port, and $15,000 out of the general hospital fund, for the erection of a marine hospital. The same proposal, which was renewed in 1803, was accepted November 2, 1804, with the provision, made on the part of the council, that the city should be allowed to levy a duty on tonnage of vessels to supply any deficiency that might result from building and maintaining the hospital. The City Council assumed the charge of sick and disabled seamen at the port of Charleston in April, 1805, and, one year thereafter, Congress gave its assent to an Act of the Legislature of South Carolina, imposing a tonnage duty of six cents on vessels entering Charleston from any foreign port, which was afterwards increased to ten cents. No further steps appear to have been taken when Mr. Dallas, then Secretary of the Treasury, purchased a site at Hampstead for $5,500, paying for the same out of the marine hospital fund. Years passed on, and, in 1830, Congress appropriated $25,000 for a hospital, $12,050 of which were paid to the City Council for interest on $15,000, from January, 1818, to May, 1830, for indemnity for damages sustained from being obliged to provide a building for a hospital in consequence of the failure of the Treasury Department to furnish $15,000 for the erection of a marine hospital, according to the proposition of the Secretary of the Treasury made in 1802.

In 1831, work was commenced on the site which had been provided at Hampstead sixteen years before, but as no secure foundation could be obtained without the driving of piles, the site was abandoned and another was selected in the city of Charleston where a hospital was finally completed in December, 1833, of which the City Council was notified to take charge and assume the care and management, as previously provided.

Before taking charge of the hospital, the City Council appointed a committee to examine the building, who, in their report thereon, represented that the roof leaked in several places, that the piazza floors, six in number, were so laid as to throw the water on the building instead of throwing it off, thereby keeping the walls damp to such an extent as to be conspicuous on the plastering within. Several other serious defects were represented to exist. The leasing of the marine hospital at Charleston to the city authorities appears not to have been attended with happy results, as seamen made complaints to the Department that they had been discharged from the hospital and the rooms appropriated to other purposes (6).

Others than Dr. Woodworth indicate that this hospital and medical care, in many instances farmed out through second parties, was not satisfactory to its recipients. The Secretary of the Navy had this to say in 1810 as to conditions in a specific hospital:

To give you some faint idea of what is called the hospital at this station, imagine to yourself an old mill, situated upon the margin of a mill-pond, where every high tide flows, from twelve to fifteen inches, upon the lower floor, and there deposits a quantity of mud and sediment, and which has no other covering to protect the sick from the inclemency of the season than a common clap-board outside, without any lining or ceiling on the inside (6).

To some extent, of course, this testimony would be of a selected nature, for at the time the Navy was interested in obtaining legislation that would remove medical care of their personnel from the Act for the relief of seamen and make of it a direct Navy function.

Such an Act was passed in 1811 (7). In 1848, a definite effort was made to reverse the original situation and have the marine hospitals become a part of the Navy system. Then a surgeon in the Navy, Ruschenburger, commented as follows:

> The physicians of marine hospitals in the United States, it is believed, are generally changed with every administration of the general government at Washington. They serve no apprenticeship in the service. . . . The arrangement of appointments and contracting out for hospital supplies places considerable patronage at the disposal of the Treasury Department and of Collectors, if they be pleased to avail themselves of it for political purposes (8).

But not all complaints against the medical care provided for seamen were limited to the Navy, or incident to the latter's wish for independence and growth. Dr. J. B. Hamilton, Supervising Surgeon General of the Marine Hospital Service in 1882, in his report for that year, insists that in many ways the Service was much better than was formerly the case. To prove how bad it once was, he provides a substantiating document marked "Exhibit B." This is somewhat staccato and disconnected in style, and appears to be made up of extracts from previous reports on conditions in marine hospitals. The part of the Exhibit that sets forth the earlier conditions is printed below as it appears in the Report for the year 1882.

Condition of Hospitals Prior to 1871

Regulations not uniform. "Hospital at Mobile as distinct and different from that at Norfolk or New Orleans as if one were a hotel and the other a hospital." "In one the surgeon resides in the hospital grounds, and in other he pursues his private business in the circuit of his city, and an assistant represents him for months in the wards of his hospital." "Here the surgeon selects his own steward, there the collector of his district makes the appointment himself." (Edwards-Loring report to Congress, 1849–'50.)

"Regulation of the Treasury Department a dead letter, each port being more or less a law unto itself." . . .

"System of inspections rarely carried out. The two hospitals where the 'board of visitors' made their visits were in worse condition than the average; far better results would be obtained by appointing the *unsuccessful* candidates for surgeon and collector as inspectors." (Report of Dr. J. S. Billings, U.S. Army, to the Secretary of the Treasury, October 18, 1869.)

"The majority of the patients at Cleveland Hospital dissatisfied with their medical treatment, and complained with regard to the quality and quantity of the food given them. Mattresses filthy, no bed-spreads, no surgical instruments." (Report of Drs. Stewart and Billings, October 14, 1869.) Medical officers subsisted by the Service.

No seamen treated at dispensaries; out-patients admitted to hospital, and one day accounted for, even for the most trivial complaints. . . .

Medical Officers—How Appointed Prior to 1873

At first, the President reserved to himself the appointment of surgeons to the hospitals, (letter of Secretary Gallatin, April 19, 1809,) but their appointment afterward became a perquisite of the collector of customs, and was viewed as such. No abuses or incompetence were likely to be exposed unless the collector were willing.

Transfers of station were not customary, medical officers being appointed to a particular port, and not to the general service; hence, after appointment, they became engaged in private practice, not infrequently to the extent of neglect of the hospital patients intrusted to their care by the Government (9).

The seamen of New York also protested to Congress in a sort of round robin in 1822.

The number of seamen who enter and depart from this harbor varies with the fluctuations of commerce; one year may show a list of one thousand sick and disabled seamen; another may

show two thousand. And yet a regulation has been made, and
rigidly executed, by the agent of the Government, that no more
than sixty seamen can be received into the New York Hospital.
. . . Seamen, who have paid hospital money for twenty years
and more . . . are compelled, in the dark and desolating hour of
sickness and misfortune, to ask for relief at the doors of the hospital and to ask in vain. . . . The Government have thought
proper, also, to say, through their agent in New York, to the seamen who sail into her port, "You shall not be in our hospital
more than four months, nor shall you be there at all if suffering
under venereal diseases, or if afflicted with mania, or if there is
no hope of your recovery" (10).

Not all the difficulties, however, arose because of restrictions and
poor quality of care. Trouble developed in another area, in that
there was sharp political pressure to build a hospital here or there.
Sites were purchased only to be abandoned later as unfit. Hospitals were built and never occupied; or built at considerable cost
and later sold for a song. In his first report, Supervising Surgeon
Woodworth cites these things. He refers to a hospital at Macdonough, opposite New Orleans, completed at a cost of $122,772.70 in
1849. In June, 1858, being inundated by the Mississippi, it was
abandoned. In 1866 it was sold for $300, which amount, Dr. Wood-
worth remarks, somewhat plaintively, "does not appear to have
been paid into the Treasury." Even before the Macdonough hospital was abandoned, "a site for a second marine hospital was selected in a swamp back of the City, New Orleans, and the creation
thereon of an immense cast-iron hospital was commenced in 1856."
A half million dollars was spent to bring this to partial completion.
It had never been used as a marine hospital up to 1872, and Dr.
Woodworth at that time felt it better "that it should be suffered to
rust away than to occupy it."

Not only were there problems as to quality of medical care of
seamen and the building of hospitals at seaports, but unusual ques-

tions arose at new places. Thus, as the country developed, lake and river ports arose in the interior. Was a sailor on the Great Lakes a seaman, and why could not hospitals be built at river towns? Dr. Woodworth described the problem in this way:

> The administration of the fund on this principle, * worked the greatest hardships in the new cities and towns which sprang up on the banks of the western lakes and rivers, where few accommodations were to be had for the care of sick strangers left helpless upon their shores. Those who engaged in the commerce of the western rivers were subjected to climatic changes that were to them very pernicious. The numbers who perished in the long-descending voyages of the flat-bottomed boats which left the upper waters of the Mississippi and its tributaries, in summer and early autumn, to find a market for the fruits of their toil, at New Orleans, were very great. Nothing was more common than for two out of the five hands who generally managed these boats to die; and it sometimes happened that the whole crew perished from disease, and that the boat with its cargo was left deserted.

> The steamboats ascending the Mississippi and its tributaries brought up every year a great number of deck passengers, chiefly the sons of farmers returning from their flat-boat voyages, many of whom died on board, while others were left on shore at the river towns helpless and among strangers. The cholera epidemic of 1832 and 1834 added greatly to the catalogue of ills. Moved by a feeling of common humanity for the large class of our young men who had surrendered the endearments of a life spent at home, and united their fortunes with strangers by embarking in the more daring, precarious, and toilsome interests of commerce—a pursuit, more than most others, beset with temptations to risk of health and life, to recklessness of character and insensibility to future wants—sensible also of the sufferings attendant upon such an improvident life, whole communities,

---

* It was claimed that the fund was to be considered as auxiliary to the provisions made by the municipal authorities, rather than as a full compensation for the relief which was due to the wants of sick and disabled seamen. In view of the inadequacy of the fund, a more liberal ruling was impracticable.

both on the seaboard and in the interior districts, petitioned Congress for additional appropriations and the enactment of laws providing increased facilities for the relief of this unfortunate class. From one port it was reported that no better place could be offered to sick seamen than the warehouses and deserted tenements along the wharf; from another, that they had to be sent to the city almshouse, which was also connected with a penitentiary for common vagrants and petty convicts; and from another, the sad story was told that seamen, sick with various diseases—cholera, smallpox, etcetera—were often forced promiscuously into the same chamber, where the dying and the dead were alike neglected.

The appeals, made alike to the munificence of the Government and to its high obligation to protect and cherish the interests of commerce, were not unheeded by the representatives of the people. Congress passed an Act, which was approved March 3, 1837, authorizing the Secretary of War to appoint a Board of Medical Officers of the Army to select and purchase sites for marine hospitals on the Mississippi and Ohio rivers and Lake Erie. The board appointed in pursuance of the Act, consisting of Surgeon B. F. Harney and Assistant Surgeons H. L. Hieskell and J. M. Cuyler, made their report to the Secretary of War in November, 1837, having selected sites, ranging from eight to eighteen acres in extent, at the ports of Natchez, Mississippi; Napoleon, Arkansas; St. Louis, Missouri; Paducah and Louisville, Kentucky; Wheeling, Virginia, and Cleveland, Ohio. The board recommended that the buildings to be constructed should be planned with a view to future enlargement, without injury to symmetry, et cetera. It is a significant fact that the plans for marine hospitals, drawn by Mr. Robert Mills, architect, in the year 1837, have been followed by the Government, without material change, down to the hospital now being constructed at Chicago, Illinois. Marine hospitals were subsequently built at all the ports recommended by the Army Board, except Wheeling. Pittsburgh claimed and finally obtained the hospital at that port instead of at Wheeling. Considerable delay in erecting hospitals at the points selected on the western waters appears to

have resulted from placing the subject under the direction of
the Secretary of War. The Secretary of the Treasury, in a letter
addressed to the chairman of the Senate Committee on Commerce, dated May 3, 1844, said, in reference to an appropriation
for a marine hospital at Cleveland: "This Department has no information as to what has heretofore been done in the premises,
the subject having been placed by the Act of May 3, 1837, under
the direction of the Secretary of War" (11).

Evidently, the Secretary of the Treasury, theoretically in charge
of administering the Act for relief of seamen, was not at all happy
that Congress in 1837 had brought the Army into the picture so far
as concerned planning and building marine hospitals. Congress
was undoubtedly justified in this, for the marine hospital program
had gotten into a deplorable condition under previous Secretaries
of the Treasury. Factors contributing to this situation have already
been mentioned. They are well summarized by Leigh, as follows:

During its first seventy years of activity, the Service had ac-
quired practically all the administrative disabilities associated
with Jeffersonian and Jacksonian democracy: its personnel was
the object of party spoils; its purchase of supplies was an adjunct
to party machinery; its decentralization and lack of central supervision were almost complete; its hospitals were a part of the
annual distribution from the Congressional pork barrel; as a
means of governmentally-supervised sickness insurance it was a
fiscal failure requiring annual doles from Congress to keep it
solvent and functioning; on account of enforced parsimony it
was also very far from offering any guaranty of medical aid to
the sailors even at the principal ports (12).

Of significance in relation to public health work is the fact that
remedies *were* instituted. Apparently the Secretary of the Treasury
(George S. Boutwell) felt that something must be done to improve
the situation. In 1869 he arranged for John Shaw Billings, then a
medical officer of the Army, to investigate and recommend. He de-

tailed a Dr. Stewart (apparently employed by the Treasury Department under a customs officer title) to assist. On the Billings-Stewart report was built the Act of 1870, by which the Service was reorganized and directed on a national basis.

The newly proposed legislation was designated as Senate (Bill) No. 489 and the completed legislation was entitled, "An Act to Reorganize the Marine-Hospital Service and to provide for the relief of sick and disabled seamen" (13). In the bill it was proposed that the amount deducted from seamen's wages be trebled: from twenty cents a month to "two cents a day." Forty cents per month was the compromise finally adopted. The second provision in the new Act was for a nationalized supervision, under medical auspices: a supervising surgeon was to be appointed. What the Secretary of the Treasury seems really to have wanted was to have Billings detailed to direct the Service; and in the bill was a proposal that the Supervising Surgeon might be a medical officer of the Army or Navy. This was objected to and eliminated (14).

From the Senate's discussion of the subject, one cannot escape the conclusion that relief of seamen and the hospital building program, particularly the latter, had become an irritant and an embarrassment to Congress. Even the proponents of the new bill admitted this, and their principal argument was that the proposed measures would eliminate recognized evils. Doubtless many of the statements made were extreme, but the temper of the discussion is shown by such passages as the following:

> My judgment . . . is that true economy requires that we should either sink the marine hospitals, every one of them, or sell them. If there has been any one inexcusable, intolerable abuse in the public expenditures of this country, it has been in this matter of building marine hospitals. . . . It was a favorite mode of starting a new town in the West, if it was anywhere on a stream or on a good sized puddle, to get an appropriation for a marine hospital (14).

There was revived again the old discussion of just why the Federal Government should be concerned with this particular group of the population. Seamen were described as "the most improvident class of men that ever trod the earth. . . . They are improvident; they expend all their means. After a long voyage of months or years they go ashore and have their frolic. They bear your flag upon every sea. They are, in a sense, representatives of our commercial interests. They have always been treated somewhat as wards of a kind Government."

Some argued that if the seamen were independently occupied, they ought to pay entirely for their own care. "Either they are at work for the Government or for themselves. If for us, let us be honest and take care of them when they cannot work for you. If they are at work for themselves then be honest and let them take care of themselves."

Opponents of the bill could see no possible reason for employing a chief medical officer who would be paid a salary to travel over the country at the government's expense, but in spite of opposition the Act was passed and, from an administrative standpoint, a national service was created.

The reorganized hospital program of 1870 and the newly nationalized Marine Hospital Service soon felt the guiding hand of a strong and foreseeing directing officer. Dr. John M. Woodworth had been in health work in Chicago, and had served as a surgeon in the Federal Army in the War between the States. Perhaps influenced by his military experience, and probably under the sound advice of Billings, he organized the new corps and its procedures along military lines. He insisted upon a searching and impartial entrance examination, rather completely removed tenure of office and promotion from politics, and instituted other sound measures that remain in effect today.

In his 1873 report, he evidences considerable apprehension as to the physical condition of those employed as seamen. He quotes data indicating that from 10 to 25 per cent of crews were physically unfit for duty. He says, splitting an infinitive in the process, that "while the Service, under the operation of the present Act, gives promise of becoming eventually self-sustaining, the percentage of relief made necessary by causes which are, in a large measure, avoidable, is so great as to materially retard this desideratum" (15). He urged that physical examinations before shipping be made a requirement and that "in order to avoid the miscarriage of the measure . . . medical officers of the Service might be employed to make such examinations without charge either to owner or men." That this was a real interest and not just a pious hope for prevention, is indicated by the fact that in his next report (1874) Dr. Woodworth goes further. He devotes a section to "Preventive Medicine in the Service," and opens the discussion thus:

> While the primary object of the Service as defined by statute is the "relief of sick and disabled seamen," the duty of preventing, in whatever degree, such sickness and disability, is also conceived to be within its scope. Hence, preventive medicine, which is receiving from the profession a continually-increasing amount of attention, has not been lost sight of in its bearing upon the physical welfare of seamen; and the medical officers of the Service have been invited to study and report upon the conditions of sea-life with a view to devising measures for the preservation of the sailor's health and his protection from disease (16).

Response to this invitation to medical officers of the Service is manifested by papers they prepared. These form a part of the Marine Hospital Reports. They deal with hazards peculiar to seamen or abundantly shared by them, and bear such significant titles as *Hygiene of the Forecastle; Unseaworthy Sailors; Preventable Dis-*

eases of the Great Lakes; The Cause and Prevention of Disease Among River-men; Syphilis: The Scourge of the Sailor and the Public Health. In the report of 1874 and in others prepared by Woodworth, the epidemic aspects of yellow fever are given much space and in general he evidences an astonishing interest in preventive medicine and public health.

A detailed examination of the medical and hospital aspects of federal service, in the period between Woodworth's appointment and the present, would not further the purposes of this discussion. A number of elements of possible interest to the future may, however, be listed as follows:

1. The requirement that beneficiaries of the Marine Hospital Service contribute to its support was eliminated by an Act approved June 26, 1884 (17). Part of the expenses were to be paid by a special tonnage tax, part by general taxation. Tonnage tax was eliminated in 1905 (18), and from then on relief of sick and disabled seamen (and certain others) was supported by funds in the Treasury, not otherwise appropriated.

That there was this transition from a medical service, supported through compulsory deductions from the payrolls of its beneficiaries, to a benefit supported by a general tax is a matter worthy of considerable present thought.

2. The system of indirect and contract medical service, at first entirely localized, has become strongly centralized. Except in minor instances, part-time physicians have given place to full-time medical officers, employed upon a career basis, though consultation staffs (part-time private physicians) are maintained. From this, alternate arguments might be advanced: it might be concluded that locally autonomous and non-centrally directed medical services have proven themselves impracticable; or, with a different approach and attitude, it might be concluded that the tendency of the Federal Government, in operating a medical service, is to sup-

plant local independence with centrally directed bureaucratic control, replacing part-time physicians with salaried medical officers.

3. Supervising Surgeon Woodworth was in favor of "constructing all hospitals of wood, and destroying them after ten or fifteen years, both as a sanitary and economical measure, and building new ones in their stead" (19). It is a far cry from this concept to the present when, in addition to contract and special hospitals, the Public Health Service now has 26 Marine Hospitals of the First Class, containing some 6,500 beds. The construction of these hospitals compares favorably with the highest grade municipal and private hospitals of the nation. They are all approved by the American Hospital Association.

4. Significant of what may happen in federal medical care is that beneficiaries of the Service have burst completely the bounds of any possible definition of "seamen." Beneficiaries in 1943 included: American merchant seamen, Coast Guard personnel, Coast Guard dependents, Coast and Geodetic Survey personnel; Coast and Geodetic Survey dependents; seamen, Engineer Corps and Army Transport Service; seamen, not enlisted or commissioned, from other government vessels; seamen from foreign vessels; Public Health Service officers and employees; persons afflicted with leprosy; Employees' Compensation Commission; immigrants and alien seamen; Army and Selective Service; Navy and Marine Corps; Veterans' Administration; Civilian Conservation Corps; Work Projects Administration; National Youth Administration; former enrollees, Civilian Conservation Corps; Maritime Service; miscellaneous (20).

5. Increase of activities in this once quite limited federal program may be appreciated partially by comparing number of patients treated and costs of the United States Marine Hospital Services for 1872 (21) with those of the United States Public Health Service for 1943 (22):

	United States Marine Hospital Service 1872	*United States Public Health Service* 1943
Number sick and disabled receiving hospital care	12,302	137,227
Number hospital days	405,814	2,517,248
Average days of patient in hospital	32.9	18.3
Number cared for, outpatient	854	1,190,215
Number visits, outpatient	–	3,067,577
Total cared for, hospital and outpatient	13,156	1,327,436
Number of deaths	501	1,720
Case fatality ratio	4.3	1.3
Cost per patient day	$0.976	$4.23 (1941)
Total expenditures for all Public Health Service activities, approx.	$396,263.11	$59,764,250.78

In effect then, for good or ill, this federal medical service has tended to expand, to eliminate local participation by focusing centripetally, and to become more efficient than when under local, part-time auspices. Further, it is of no little significance that this medical care program, designed to be supported by payments from those benefited, has for the last sixty years been supported from general taxation: general taxation for medical care of 1) employees of certain government services, as Coast Guard and Geodetic Survey, and 2) a narrow segment of the population (seamen) *not* employed by government.

Discussion of the work of the United States Public Health Service and its possible significance will be resumed shortly. For the moment it seems wise to interpolate a note as to certain early and somewhat incidental health laws enacted in the late eighteenth century.

Incidental Early Federal Legislation Relating to Public Health

While the Act for relief of sick and disabled seamen was the first federal legislation that provided medical care for a certain segment of the civilian population and is generally considered as the nucleus around which the United States Public Health Service developed, it was not the first federal Act relating to health and medical matters. In this field, there were at least three other laws passed prior to 1798. Section 8 of an "Act for the government and regulation of Seamen in the merchants service," July 20, 1790, required "that every ship or vessel belonging to a citizen or citizens of the United States, of the burthen of one hundred and fifty tons or upwards, navigated by ten or more persons in the whole, and bound on a voyage without the limits of the United States, shall be provided with a chest of medicines" (23).

A second bit of public health legislation was an Act passed in 1794 which provided that Congress might be convened other than at the seat of government during times of epidemic (24). This Act was not of any particular significance so far as concerns the health of the nation, but as with subsequent and somewhat similar federal and state legislation, it suggests something for consideration today and in the future. It is this: legislative bodies have been inclined to act on health matters affecting institutions and beneficiaries of government more quickly than on those that affect the public as a whole. Thus at the time that this particular Act was passed Philadelphia, the seat of government, had been having rather bitter experiences with yellow fever. Recognizing that recurring epidemics might make it impossible to conduct the affairs of government there, Congress provided for the removal of itself from the scene, if necessary. It evidenced no attempt to prevent the outbreak of disease or to do anything about it if it occurred, but chose rather the alternative of leaving the field to the epidemic. Another illustration of the relationship between closeness of problem and legislative action is seen in the previously discussed Act for the relief of merchant seamen. Here there was a chain of circumstances that made seamen, as a class, a serious problem to Congress; and action was taken to remove the difficulty. A similar situation was to be noted in state public health work when tuberculosis pavilions were provided for psychopathic institutions and penitentiaries, but not for the general public. The same tendency is exemplified in that federal legislation which established St. Elizabeths Hospital: one kind or another of federal ward or beneficiary became insane and there was no way of solving the problem other than by Congressional action which would provide some place to put these people. It would seem somewhat paradoxical that prisoners and insane persons should be considered more peculiarly the wards of government than are ordinary citizens, but the records are clear. This point was raised only recently in hearings on a bill to codify the laws relating to the United States Public Health Service and its activities:

> Congressman Reece: ". . . Why should a convict be given preferential consideration to an addict (narcotic) who has not committed an offense?"
>
> Surgeon General Parran: "That is a very fair question, Mr. Reece. The only answer I know of is that once a person is convicted, the Federal Government must care for him somewhere. . . ." (25)

Development of Federal Quarantine

Foreign quarantine. A third health law (26), preceding the Act for the relief of seamen, was passed in 1796. This related to quarantine. It provided only for federal cooperation with states and localities in enforcing state and local quarantine relating to ships.

It should not be assumed, however, that even in 1796 all members of the Congress subscribed to the thesis that quarantine is essentially a state function. Actually, in the original bill there was a clause that would have given the Federal Government a basis of authority for making uniform the quarantine procedures at the various ports in the several states. The argument in the House of

Representatives on this phase of the proposed legislation was spirited (27). Mr. Smith of Maryland said that each individual state might have its own health laws, but the performance of quarantine was in the direction of the General Government. He felt that the President of the United States ought to be empowered to designate the place where vessels should perform quarantine, to enforce the performance, and to determine at what time of the year it should commence and end. He denied that there was any authority in the State Governments to regulate quarantine, for they could not command the officer of a port to use force to prevent a vessel entering their ports; the authority over him was in the General Government. Another Mr. Smith, of South Carolina, said the Constitution did not give to the State Governments the power of stopping vessels from coming to the ports. He further said: "Epidemic diseases imported affect the United States at large. They do not merely affect the city where first imported but they obstruct the commerce of all others; they not only embarrass the commerce but injure the revenues of the United States."

Many members of the House, however, expressed themselves as being convinced that "each independent state had a right to legislate on this subject for itself" and in the final vote, 46 to 23, that clause which would have made quarantine essentially a federal function was eliminated from the bill. As passed, the bill simply provided "that the President of the United States be and is hereby authorized to direct the revenue officers and the officers commanding ports, and revenue cutters, to aid in the execution of quarantine and also the execution of the health laws of the states, respectively, in such manner as may appear to him necessary."

It is interesting to note that when the bill was sent to the Senate for concurrence that body suggested an amendment whereby after the first word "that" there be inserted "until general regulations relative to quarantine are made by law." Although this amend-

ment was lost, it cast a shadow which was finally to gain substance
in the decision of the United States Supreme Court, nearly a hundred years later (1886), in a case brought to it through litigation
between the Board of Health of Louisiana and Morgan's Louisiana
and Texas Railroad and Steamship Company. The case involved
the right of the State Board of Health of Louisiana to charge fees
for quarantine services performed. The Court found for the Louisiana State Board of Health and as part of a lengthy opinion had the
following to say:

> For the period of nearly a century, since the government was
> organized, Congress has passed no quarantine law, nor any other
> law to protect the inhabitants of the United States against the
> invasion of contagious and infectious diseases from abroad; and
> yet during the early part of the present century, for many years
> the cities of the Atlantic coast, from Boston and New York to
> Charleston, were devastated by the yellow fever. In later times
> the cholera has made similar invasions; and the yellow fever has
> been unchecked in its fearful course in the Southern cities, New
> Orleans especially, for several generations. During all this time
> the Congress of the United States never attempted to exercise
> this or any other powers to protect the people from the ravages
> of these dreadful diseases. No doubt they believed that the
> power to do this belonged to the States. Or, if it ever occurred to
> any of its members that Congress might do something in that
> way, they probably believed that what ought to be done could
> be better and more wisely done by the authorities of the States
> who were familiar with the matter.
> But it may be conceded that whenever Congress shall under-
> take to provide for the commercial cities of the United States a
> general system of quarantine, or shall confide the execution of
> the details of such a system to a National Board of Health, or to
> local boards, as may be found expedient, all State laws on the
> subject will be abrogated, at least so far as the two are incon-
> sistent. But, until this is done, the laws of the State on the sub-
> ject are valid (28).

Although federal quarantine legislation seems eventually to have followed the suggestion laid down in the Supreme Court decision, the procedure during the first seventy-five years of the nineteenth century consisted essentially in federal cooperation in the enforcement of state and local quarantine laws and, in general, the Federal Congress rather carefully avoided any action that might conflict with state authority in this field. In 1878 the Federal Government went a little further in that there was enacted a national law (29) designed to prevent the introduction of contagious and infectious diseases into the United States. This law reiterated previous requirements that vessels might not pass the boundary line between the United States and any foreign country contrary to the quarantine laws of any one of said United States, but provided a clause "or except in the manner and subject to the regulations to be prescribed as hereinafter provided." Section II of the Act, however, immediately countered the exception above by saying that rules and regulations made by the Surgeon General of the Marine Hospital Service and approved by the President "shall not conflict with or impair any sanitary or quarantine laws or regulations of any state or municipal authorities now existing or which may hereafter be enacted." Nevertheless, this legislation of 1878 did bring the Marine Hospital Service into the picture and provided "that whenever at any port of the United States any state or municipal quarantine system may now or may hereafter exist, the officers or agents of such system shall, upon the application of the respective state or municipal authorities, be authorized and empowered to act as officers or agents of the national quarantine system." And it further provided for consular report on the sanitary condition of ports from which vessels might come.

In the meantime, public opinion was tending to press for national action to prevent the importation of contagious diseases. The constant recurrence of yellow fever epidemics, the memory of the cholera epidemics beginning in 1832, and the comparatively recent experience with the cholera outbreak of 1873 contributed to this. Shipping interests, too, expressed themselves as greatly discommoded by the varying and sometimes arbitrary quarantine regulations that existed in the many ports of the United States, though it may here be remarked parenthetically that these interests did not, at first, acquiesce in national quarantine when it was achieved. By this time another force made itself felt. This was a group of physicians in the American Public Health Association who urged a national department of health. Needless to say, there was a vast amount of argument and difference of opinion, but finally, under an Act of 1879 (30), provision was made "for a National Board of Health to have charge of interstate and foreign quarantine." This law repealed that part of the Quarantine Act of 1878 which gave quarantine powers to the Marine Hospital Service, these responsibilities being transferred to the new Board. Congress evidently regarded this Board of Health as somewhat of an expediency, for under the Act it was to function in interstate and foreign quarantine only four years.

The history of the National Board of Health forms an interesting and somewhat significant chapter in the development of public health in the United States, but for present purposes it need be said only that, in spite of the support of many strong and sound men, the Board encountered violent opposition. No small part of this opposition came from the Marine Hospital Service, from which had been taken quarantine responsibilities. Many of the southern state health officers, too, perhaps as a part of their conviction as to states' rights, opposed the National Board of Health. This was particularly the case with Dr. Joseph Jones, President of the Louisiana State Board of Health, 1880–1884. He was evidently a vigorous man with definite ideas and a willingness to express them. He did not hesitate to speak of "the insolent pretensions of the National Board of Health with its odious system of espionage and intermeddling" (31). Officially the National Board of Health did not go out of existence until 1893, but actually it ceased to function at the end of four years, when quarantine duties were restored to the Marine Hospital Service.

The next development in the Federal Government's assumption of responsibility and authority in quarantine of ships from foreign ports is to be found in an Act of 1893 (32) which in its opening paragraph says rather bluntly "that it shall be unlawful for any merchant ship or other vessel from any foreign port or place to enter any port of the United States except in accordance with the provisions of this Act and with such rules and regulations of state and municipal authorities as may be made in pursuance of or consistence with this Act." While this new legislation recognized regulations of state and municipal authorities, it boldly stated, and for the first time, that such regulations must be in pursuance of or consistent with this federal law. Perhaps here the cue was taken from the Supreme Court decision of 1886, previously referred to. This Act of 1893 further made provision that if state or municipal health authorities did not have adequate laws, they would be supplemented by federal laws, and if they failed or refused to enforce proper rules and regulations, the Federal Government might supersede them. Finally, provision was made that the Federal Government might purchase municipal and state quarantine stations if necessary to the United States.

This summary of the early development of federal health service may be brought to a close by stating that, with the passage of years, all state and municipal quarantine stations have been purchased by the Federal Government, and that all foreign quarantine in the United States is now conducted by the Federal Government through the United States Public Health Service. The last station and service to be absorbed was that of the Port of New York in 1921.

Some of the details presented above may seem unnecessary; possibly they are. Nevertheless, there is a purpose in presenting them, for it seems desirable to follow a trend toward nationalizing of health activities; to demonstrate the fact that when interstate and international questions are involved, state or local administration of public health work is inadequate and confusing; and to show that the Federal Government, through the process of associating health activities with others over which it holds unquestioned jurisdiction, has within it a potentiality for absorbing state and local services.

There seems to be no doubt that, if approached from the standpoint of control of communicable diseases, quarantine measures, including those designed to prevent the introduction of such diseases from abroad, are inherent in the police power of each of the several states. At the same time, it must be recognized that the vessels which might bring these diseases are engaged primarily in commerce, that commerce involves international treaties and agreements, that states may not make international treaties and agreements. When this aspect is given consideration, a strong argument can be advanced for federal assumption of this responsibility. The record indicates that foreign quarantine service under federal direction has the great advantage of uniformity, and that it eliminates bargain regulations that might attract vessels to ports with lax requirements. Most of the cities and states had clumsily administered and not even nearly effective quarantine procedures. The outstanding exception to this was the Port of New York, upon whose regulations and requirements much of the federal quarantine system was built.

Interstate quarantine. In the Act of 1879, creating the National

Board of Health, that federal agency was empowered to enforce interstate quarantine measures, but this authority was not conveyed to the Marine Hospital Service when the National Board of Health became inactive. However, experience had indicated that, in the case of yellow fever and cholera, at least, introduction of epidemic disease at a given port did not always mean that the problem would remain confined to that port or even to the state in which it might be located.

In 1890, therefore, Congress provided a law (33) that, in effect, gave the Marine Hospital Service authority to promulgate and execute regulations for the interstate control of cholera, yellow fever, smallpox, and plague. The Act of 1893 (32), although mainly concerned with strengthening port quarantine, gave additional power in interstate quarantine to the Federal Government by two simple devices. First, to the clause which conferred authority to prevent the "introduction of infectious or contagious diseases into the United States from foreign countries" was added "or from one State or Territory . . . into another State or Territory." Second, instead of listing in the Act itself those diseases in which the Federal Government would take action, the expression "cholera, yellow fever, or other contagious or infectious diseases" was used. The words, "other contagious or infectious diseases," made it possible to meet changing problems by regulations without further specific authority from Congress.

The responsibility and power granted under the Acts of 1890 and 1893 are sufficiently broad to have permitted the Public Health Service, in interstate quarantine, to encroach upon and perhaps supersede state authority, as happened in foreign quarantine. This would have called for a far less broad interpretation of law and the Constitution than has been made to cover a number of other federal activities. That the Public Health Service did not take this course is reassuring to those who look with apprehension upon the growth of federal health activities at the expense of state and local health administration. Only on rare occasions has the United States Public Health Service exercised its authority in the control of epidemic diseases. Plague in San Francisco, in the early years of this century, made federal control obviously and clearly necessary. It was invoked also in the poliomyelitis epidemic of 1916 in New York. In all routine situations, however, in which the spread of disease has been potentially an interstate problem, the Service has brought about agreement between the state health authorities concerned and has in many instances lent trained officers to assist in control activities. In no small degree, this arrangement has been made practicable, and difficulties have been prevented or adjusted, through the Annual Conference of State and Territorial Health Officers with the Surgeon General. This procedure was authorized and directed by Congress in 1902 (34).

Closely related to interstate quarantine is another Act, passed in 1902 (35). This provided for regulation of the interstate sale of viruses, serums, toxins, and analogous products. As in foreign and interstate quarantine, the Federal Government approached this problem not directly as one concerning health, but obliquely and through its responsibilities in interstate commerce. Only two comments seem necessary here. One is that, although this Act generally assures consumers that antitoxins, vaccines, et cetera, will be potent and free from dangerous extraneous ingredients or contaminants, it exercises no control over such products when their sale is limited to the state in which manufactured. That is the business of the state concerned. The second pertinent comment on this Act is that it bears only upon so-called biological products. It has nothing to do with food or drugs, this responsibility being rather amazingly dispersed and to some extent duplicated through the activities of a number of other federal agencies.

Development of States' Relations

The United States Public Health Service occupies an enviable and commendable position in its relationships with the health authorities of the several states. Through grants-in-aid, through loan of personnel, through consultation and careful observation of protocol, this Service is perhaps, of all federal agencies in any field, the one which exhibits the practicability of coordinated action between a federal union as a whole and its individual constituent members. Indirectly and intangibly, too, through high standards of performance and through demonstration and efficiency, the Public Health Service has raised the level of work performed in every county, city, and state health department with which it has had even indirect contact.

Federal grants-in-aid in public health work came about only gradually, though the idea was proposed as long ago as 1879 when the bill (30) creating the short-lived National Board of Health was under consideration. Dr. Cabell, the Chairman of that Board, states that Section 2 of this bill as passed by the House of Representatives contained the following:

> It shall also aid in the work of State Boards of Health, and of State and municipal authorities, by such means and to such an extent as may seem to it necessary and desirable. And for this purpose it is authorized to pay a certain portion of the expenses of such State Boards of Health or quarantine authorities at its discretion. Provided that the amount so paid shall in no case exceed one-half the total expenses for any such Board or quarantine authority. And provided further, that such reports and information as may be required by the National Board of Health shall be furnished by the State Boards and quarantine authorities so aided (36).

Section 4, according to Dr. Cabell, appropriated $500,000 for carrying out the provision of Section 2. Dr. Cabell believes that in transcribing the bill for Senate action the clerk responsible did not include this provision. In any event, it did not become a part of the law of 1879.

For most of the next third of a century, the Marine Hospital Service was preoccupied with stabilizing its two principal activities: medical care of beneficiaries and foreign quarantine. It is significant, however, that during this period its name was changed twice, first, in 1902, to the United States Public Health and Marine Hospital Service (34), and in 1912 to the designation it now bears, the United States Public Health Service (37). These changes in title indicate that by the beginning of the present century it was acquiring additional duties, and in this process obtained funds for "Field Investigations of Public Health" in 1913. It was through this function that field studies in typhoid fever were made in the period 1914–1916, in cooperation with some sixteen states. Though officially this was investigation, in practice the work also included attempts to demonstrate effective control measures. The nature of the work and its administration brought about relationships that were new in the experience of federal, state, and local health organizations concerned. Thus was laid a foundation for mutual confidence and interdependence, and on it was built a sound cooperative program.

In 1916, Congress provided a specific appropriation for demonstrations in rural sanitation (38), wherein states that wished such work within their borders might, on agreement to pay one half the expenses, make application. The amount of federal funds available, however, was only $25,000 for the whole United States, which automatically limited the undertaking. Over a period of years, the funds available remained quite small, as will be seen from Table I.

The financial details in the period 1917–1935 are not nearly so important as are the policies, precedents, and sound federal-state relationships which were established during this time. The work

TABLE I. Amounts specifically appropriated by the Congress for the rural sanitation work of the United States Public Health Service (39)

Fiscal year	Amount	Fiscal year	Amount
1917	$ 25,000	1926	$ 75,000
1918	150,000	1927	75,000
1919	150,000	1928	265,740[a]
1920	50,000	1929	347,000
1921	50,000	1930	346,000
1922	50,000	1931	726,650[b]
1923	50,000	1932	1,949,350[c]
1924	50,000	1933	300,000
1925	74,300	1934	150,000[d]

a. Including $180,740 released from appropriation for the prevention of the spread of epidemic diseases and applied to county health work in the Mississippi flood area.

b. Including $388,650 from the special appropriation for health work in the drought-stricken area.

c. Including $1,611,350 from the special appropriation for health work in the drought-stricken area.

d. Amount actually available, $25,000.

evolved from an undertaking concerned only with methods of control of typhoid fever to a demonstration of the effectiveness of reasonably adequate local rural health departments responsible for broad community health services. As before, activities were limited because of lack of funds, but the effect of the program reached far beyond the local areas and even beyond the states in which the combined federal-state-local activities were in progress. Another result of this undertaking was in the stimulation of larger state and local appropriations. In the first place, federal aid required matching of federal grants by state, or local or other funds, or all three. This requirement stimulated the interest of the communities concerned, and they in turn made their influence felt in local appropriating bodies and state legislatures. Further, the financial aid received from the Federal Government was understood to be temporary, so far as concerned any given locality, and plans had to be made to underwrite the budget on federal withdrawal.

This experience with the use of federal money produced certain other important by-products, important for the future of the early 1930's and for the future as seen in 1945. Of significance here is the fact that by 1930 the United States Public Health Service had established a strong position of leadership in the public affairs of the nation. Part of this prestige was doubtless because it had some money to give to state health departments, but even more because the Service so performed, in terms of wisdom, fairness, and efficiency, that it attained, in the minds of state health officials and with the Congress, a confidence seldom given to a bureau of the Federal Government. Nevertheless, two things became apparent. The first was that each year the matter of obtaining state-aid funds from Congress was a touch-and-go affair, indicating that federal legislators still regarded Congressional appropriations for this activity of the Public Health Service as somewhat of an expedient, logically to be brought to a close in the not-too-distant future. Second, it was equally apparent that unless federal stimulation and aid of local health work were increased, it would require some generations to provide even a minimum of health service to all the communities of the nation.

That was about the situation in 1930, and the years since that time have not been entirely normal ones, there being successively a period of depression; a new venture in social security legislation which vastly increased federal aid to state health work; preparation for war; and war. In the circumstances, it seems reasonable to believe that at least some of the increased and intensified federal health activities arose because of unusual problems and responsibilities. While other pressures may result in continued federal participation, the present scale of grants-in-aid cannot be considered as either assured or inescapable.

The passage of the Social Security Act in 1935, with subsequent amendments, changed rather completely the financial status of the

Public Health Service so far as concerns its grants-in-aid to the states. Under Title VI of that Act it is provided that:

> For the purpose of assisting States, counties, health districts, and other political subdivisions of the States in establishing and maintaining adequate public-health services, including the training of personnel for State and local health work, there is hereby authorized to be appropriated for each fiscal year, beginning with the fiscal year ending June 30, 1940, the sum of $11,000,000 to be used as hereinafter provided (40).

The amount allotted for each state is determined on the basis of 1) population, 2) special health problems, and 3) financial needs of the respective states. Under Rules and Regulations of the Surgeon General (41), 27.5 per cent of available appropriation is set aside on a population basis: each state is allotted a proportion of this amount in the ratio of its population to the population of the United States. Forty-five per cent of the total available appropriation is set aside for distribution to the states on the basis of special health problems: "The ratio which the mean annual number of deaths in each state from pneumonia, cancer and other infectious or parasitic diseases, except influenza and syphilis, bears to the total mortality from these causes in the United States"; and 27.5 per cent on the basis of financial needs: in inverse proportion to the state's ability to raise revenue.

In making these grants, it is required that the state appropriate a like amount in relation to funds received on the basis of population and in relation to special health problems. The formula utilized is somewhat complicated and need not be developed here in detail.

The federal grants so provided are what may be called general purpose funds. In the main, they have been utilized to aid in the strengthening of state and local health organizations and in providing better programs, designed to meet problems more or less common to all localities. Although unusual health problems of an area are taken into consideration as indicated above, these federal funds are not earmarked for use against any particular disease or diseases. A good many years before, however, federal aid had been given to undertake cooperative studies on specific health problems: trachoma, pellagra, malaria. As a matter of fact, even the general program had its origin in the investigation of a particular disease, typhoid fever. Most of these diseases, however, occurred or were recognized as problems only in certain sections of the country. Programs for their control were embarked upon more as a result of professional interest, drama, and sectional pressure, than because they were considered national health problems. However, with the passage of the venereal disease Act of 1918 (42), the Federal Government undertook a program designed to reach a particular group of diseases common to all states and localities. A nation-wide program was visualized and provided for. Allocation to the several states of the funds made available by the Act was based on the ratio of the population of any given state to the total population of the United States. States must match federal grants for control of venereal diseases. There were certain other requirements, none of them seriously infringing on state sovereignty, and as a result of these requirements and the stimulation provided by grants-in-aid, practically all states launched upon a venereal disease program.

Unfortunately, this venereal disease Act arose as a war measure. It was well and carefully planned by experts, but was, of necessity, built from above downward. Such publicity and health education as attended it seem not to have been effective in convincing the public that control of venereal diseases was a national problem. In brief, as the problems of World War I became less pressing and were gradually forgotten, Congressional support of this Act dwindled from an original $1,000,000 for state aid in 1918 to nothing in the fiscal year 1925–1926. It left behind, however, certain things: a

Division of Venereal Disease Control in the United States Public Health Service; good basic venereal-disease-control laws in most of the states, with some, but not adequate, state and local control programs; and a memory of the program, a memory and experience that were to build for a more extensive and apparently more firmly rooted national venereal disease program in later years. This came into effect with the passage by Congress in 1938 of an Act to control venereal disease (43). This was essentially state-aid legislation, the original Act providing $5,000,000, with subsequent increases, for this purpose. This program is significant for it arose to a great extent because of public conviction that something ought to be done about gonorrhea and syphilis, and it represents national action in relation to a particular group of diseases: funds derived from this Act may not be used for general purposes. Similar action was taken by the Congress in 1944, in relation to tuberculosis (44) when an appropriation of $10,000,000 per annum was authorized.

Nation-wide System of Medical Care

There remains for consideration only one other phase of the activities of the United States Public Health Service. This is in connection with the possibility that that Service may, in the future, become more and more concerned with a nation-wide system of medical care. Although the question of general public medical service goes beyond the bounds of this discussion, it is important nevertheless to emphasize here that the United States Public Health Service, conducting at present what has heretofore been considered a conventional public health program, might, in the future, by Act of Congress, find itself functioning very much as in the nineteenth century, when the principal duty of the Service was the provision of medical care. Then, the hospital and curative program was limited to the barest fraction of the population; by 1950 the whole population might be beneficiaries of a federal medical care program. This possibility is exemplified by the Wagner-Murray Bill (45), introduced into the Senate in 1943. That bill contemplated administration of the proposed medical care program by the United States Public Health Service. In fact, so often did the title "Surgeon General of the United States Public Health Service" appear in the text of the bill that its opponents depicted the Surgeon General as *Gauleiter*.

Regardless of whether or not one approves of a public medical care program, such a program if, or perhaps when, it becomes a reality, seems likely to be fostered by the Federal Government. In this connection, it might be contended, as it was on the question of primary jurisdiction in foreign quarantine, that health and medical matters are essentially state functions; that the physicians are licensed to practice medicine by the state, not by the Federal Government; that the laws under which they practice are state and not federal laws. However, using again the precedent of quarantine, it must be borne in mind how that difficulty was resolved: the Federal Government won, not by direct assault, not by a contention that the states did not have primary jurisdiction in quarantine, but by the fact that the major problem involved was international commerce, rather than health, and therefore lay within federal jurisdiction. As mentioned quite often previously, the indirect approach, wherein disease control or medical care is made incidental to some other already conceded federal function, has been an established procedure for the expansion of federal health work and the basis for its rationalization. A similar course might well be adopted in relation to a national program of medical care. As a matter of fact, medical care was made incidental to the matter of employment and unemployment in the Wagner-Murray Bill, which suggests that this familiar technique will be employed in future.

There is, of course, another approach that might be pursued: grants-in-aid to states, as in Titles V and VI of the Social Security

Act. Such a procedure would undoubtedly find support in that part of the Constitution which, according to how one interprets it, either permits or commands the Federal Government to be concerned with the general welfare. Action on these lines would leave the states free to accept funds and participate or not. This would not constitute what some might designate as federal invasion of state sovereignty, for theoretically the state could take it or leave it. Actually, of course, two or three billion dollars, to be distributed among forty-eight states, plus the District of Columbia, and perhaps outlying territory, would constitute the basis for an attractive proposition. Even a million dollars is deep-voiced and persuasive, and possesses tones of command.

It is not within the scope of this discussion to argue the merits or demerits of public medical service. From the standpoint of its relation to the public health, however, it would seem pertinent to make this observation: public medical care becomes an affair of public health administration if and when the problem of the delivery of this service to the citizen is such as to necessitate organized social action. If that situation now exists, or is reached in the future, it becomes a matter of concern to government; and if government is to act in this connection, its public health organizations, that is, its health departments, would appear to be the logical agencies for administration of a program of this sort.

The Public Health Service, as of 1945

The preceding discussion has dealt largely with the evolution of individual activities in the United States Public Health Service. Coincidentally, there has been an attempt to gain an insight into the significances of these developments. It remains now to describe very briefly the present status of that Service.

For a period of nearly a century and a half (1798–1939), the Service functioned as a Bureau within the Treasury Department. It was there for no other reason than that, originally, the individuals to whom were paid the funds deducted from sailors' wages were the Collectors of Customs, officers in the Treasury Department. Then, in 1939, when the Federal Security Agency seemed on the road to stabilization, perhaps to a future as a Cabinet department concerned with welfare in general, it absorbed the Public Health Service (46). The fact that it was so transferred, and that the activities of the Children's Bureau, Department of Labor, and those of the Division of Vital Statistics, Census Bureau, Department of Commerce, were not, may point a moral to the general effect that one cannot play games with doughty Labor and majestic Commerce. It also suggests that when a federal health activity is not under the protection of some politically powerful parent (the Treasury Department was not really interested in keeping the Bureau of the Public Health Service), it has but little defense. As a matter of fact, however, the change was probably a very good one. The new arrangement is certainly better than the old and would be even better had it included transfer of a number of other federal health activities to the newly created Security Agency.

In the meantime, the Public Health Service had been growing. Aside from activities already mentioned, it was functioning in one way or another in most fields of public health. Diverse and new undertakings were being crowded into an outmoded administrative structure, and some years ago the necessity for reorganization became apparent. This was ultimately achieved by legislation which provided for the Service an anatomy in keeping with its physiology (47). The outline of organization made possible by this new Act is shown in the accompanying chart. This also indicates the scope of activities of the Public Health Service. Finally, in 1944, Congress took cognizance of the fact that since the Service's beginning in 1798 a great number of laws relating to this agency of government had been passed; that some of these laws had become

UNITED STATES PUBLIC HEALTH SERVICE

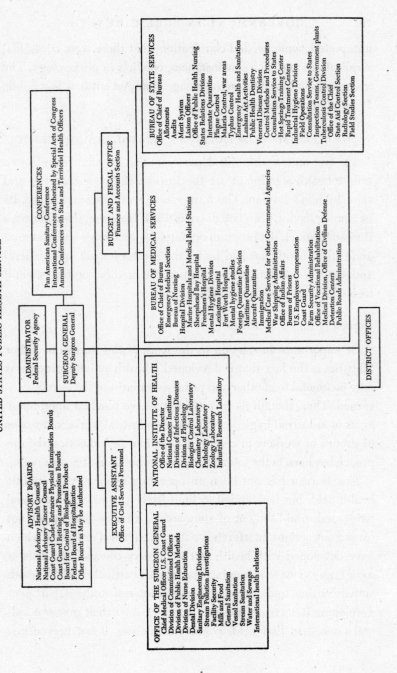

ADVISORY BOARDS
National Advisory Health Council
National Advisory Cancer Council
Coast Guard Cadet Entrance Physical Examination Boards
Coast Guard Retiring and Promotion Boards
Board for Control of Biological Products
Federal Board of Hospitalization
Other Boards as May be Authorized

ADMINISTRATOR
Federal Security Agency

CONFERENCES
Pan American Sanitary Conference
International Conferences Authorized by Special Acts of Congress
Annual Conferences with State and Territorial Health Officers

SURGEON GENERAL
Deputy Surgeon General

EXECUTIVE ASSISTANT
Office of Civil Service Personnel

BUDGET AND FISCAL OFFICE
Finance and Accounts Section

OFFICE OF THE SURGEON GENERAL
Chief Medical Officer U.S. Coast Guard
Division of Commissioned Officers
Division of Public Health Methods
Division of Nurse Education
Dental Division
Sanitary Engineering Division
Stream Pollution Investigations
Facility Security
Milk and Food
General Sanitation
Vessel Sanitation
Stream Sanitation
Water and Sewage
International health relations

NATIONAL INSTITUTE OF HEALTH
Office of the Director
National Cancer Institute
Division of Infectious Diseases
Division of Physiology
Biologics Control Laboratory
Chemistry Laboratory
Pathology Laboratory
Zoology Laboratory
Industrial Research Laboratory

BUREAU OF MEDICAL SERVICES
Office of Chief of Bureau
Emergency Medical Section
Bureau of Nursing
Hospital Division
Marine Hospitals and Medical Relief Stations
Sheepshead Bay Hospital
Freedmen's Hospital
Lexington Hospital
Fort Worth Hospital
Mental Hygiene Division
Mental hygiene studies
Foreign Quarantine Division
Maritime Quarantine
Aircraft Quarantine
Immigration
Medical Care Services for other Governmental Agencies
War Shipping Administration
Office of Indian Affairs
Bureau of Prisons
U.S. Employees Compensation
Coast Guard
Farm Security Administration
Office of Vocational Rehabilitation
Medical Division, Office of Civilian Defense
Detention Centers
Public Roads Administration

BUREAU OF STATE SERVICES
Office of Chief of Bureau
Allotments
Audits
Merit System
Liaison Officers
Office of Public Health Nursing
States Relations Division
Interstate Quarantine
Plague Control
Malaria Control, war areas
Typhus Control
Emergency Health and Sanitation
Lanham Act Activities
Public Health Dentistry
Venereal Disease Division
Control Methods and Procedures
Consultation Service to States
Hot Springs Training Center
Rapid Treatment Centers
Industrial Hygiene Division
Field Operations
Consultation Teams, Government plants
Inspection Teams, Government plants
Tuberculosis Control Division
Office of the Chief
State Aid Control Section
Radiology Section
Field Studies Section

DISTRICT OFFICES

antiquated, some needed clarification; that there were occasional duplications and, in a few instances, conflicts in phraseology. The matter was adjusted through passage of an Act entitled The Public Health Service Act (44).

The two units within this department that are significant from a public health standpoint are the Bureau of Labor Statistics and the Children's Bureau. The former is of more ancient lineage, its beginning having been laid down in 1884. However, the Children's Bureau, through the program operated by its Division of Maternal and Child Health, has had by far the greater impact upon federal and state health activities and upon the medical profession, and looms large as a potential influence.

Bureau of Labor Statistics

Of importance in relation to the work of the Bureau of Labor Statistics is the fact that it developed a health activity which was only incidental to another and principal interest of the agency concerned. Thus, though its investigations have touched upon many areas of industrial hygiene, housing of industrial workers, diseases of groups of workers in certain occupations or industries, the approach has been in the interest of labor rather than of health *per se*.

This Bureau has not been an operating agency in the public health field, but has tended to limit itself to studies, educational work, and establishment of standards. To that extent, it has not caused any serious interference with those federal programs which have developed with health as the primary concern. But it is of some importance to remember that when a particular public health activity is thus undertaken, as a minor interest to the department developing it, its mere presence may to some extent preempt federal interest in that field, possibly inhibiting, if not preventing, more active and productive operations by the principal federal health agency. In general, the likelihood that the main health program will eventually absorb such a collateral is in inverse proportion to the political and administrative strength of the department in which the collateral activity is located. In this particular instance, the department is one that has many supporters in Congress, and it is significant that, even in 1918, when the President put most civil health work of the Federal Government under the United States Public Health Service temporarily and as a war measure, the Bureau of Labor Statistics was specifically excepted.* On the other hand, the recent development of a strong industrial hygiene program in the United States Public Health Service suggests that the Bureau of Labor Statistics is not at present acting as a deterrent.

Division of Maternal and Child Health

It is somewhat difficult to assay, objectively, the health work of this federal agency, and it is likewise hard to express the significance of its present and future. Administratively, it would probably have been better had it never been born. Practically, and as a working agency, it has rendered a magnificent service in directing attention to maternal and child health and in getting something done about it. What it implies for the future is to some extent made hazy by its war-precipitated duties in a controversial field. But opposition and criticism are not new experiences for the Children's Bureau, as its work, even its right to existence, has been challenged

---

* The exceptions in this executive order, of July 1, 1918, were as follows: "This order shall not be construed as affecting the jurisdiction exercised under authority of existing law by the Surgeon General of the Army, the Surgeon General of the Navy, and the Provost Marshal General in the performance of health functions which are military in character as distinguished from civil public health duties, or as prohibiting investigations by the Bureau of Labor Statistics of vocational diseases, shop sanitation, and hygiene" (48).

up to and into the Supreme Court of the United States. Litigation arose when it became the duty of the Children's Bureau to administer the first Child Labor Law (1916) which prohibited goods produced by child labor from entering into interstate commerce. This bill was declared unconstitutional by the Supreme Court in 1918. Even before passage and nullification of that Act, the Children's Bureau had begun activities under the original statute by which it was created in 1912 (49). This had authorized investigation and report upon matters pertaining to the welfare of children. Among other things, the Bureau was especially directed to investigate infant mortality, the birth rate, and diseases of children; but in contrast to the Bureau of Labor Statistics, the Children's Bureau, though in the Department of Labor, did not have its work restricted to that group of the population concerned with what is ordinarily considered to be "labor." This is of some significance. For a number of years activities were limited, both because of inadequate funds and because its commission to "investigate and report" did not authorize an operative program.

The Children's Bureau, however, in its genesis, had the crusader spirit. In contrast with the Bureau of Labor Statistics, which has seemed satisfied to study and report and let matters rest, those interested in child health entered upon campaigns designed to do something about what they considered to be wrong. Recommendations that a more active program be authorized and supported were made and reiterated in the Bureau's Annual Reports over a period of years, and finally the first woman to enter Congress, Miss J. Rankin, introduced in 1918 a bill (50) for state aid in maternal and child care. The amounts involved in this proposed legislation amazed the seasoned and perhaps smug male public health administrators of that day: ten thousand dollars for each state plus a million dollars (to be increased to two million in five years) for additional state aid in proportion to each state's rural population, on a matching basis.

Congresswoman Rankin's bill did not become a law, but it has an important place in the development of federal public health activities. It laid the groundwork for the Sheppard-Towner Act (51), which was passed in 1921, and gave its proponents an experience that proved valuable in drafting that law. Discussion of the Rankin bill and the more successful Sheppard-Towner Act did other things. It introduced into public health consideration of a new concept: although the approach was still oblique, it proposed a public health program incident to the welfare of a group limited as to age and sex. Congress heretofore had developed health programs as part of its responsibilities in international and interstate commerce; it had directed the Bureau of Labor Statistics to gather facts on public health matters in the interest of those whose occupations might bring them under the aegis of the Department of Labor. But never before was there presented for legislative confirmation the thesis that there should be a separate public health program for women to the exclusion of men, for children under a given age to the exclusion of those older.

This new concept was, and still is, disturbing to many who felt that if it were followed to its ultimate conclusion, a coordinated and coherent federal health program would be impossible. They argued that there would be just as much logic in having the Division of School Hygiene, Department of the Interior, conduct all federal programs concerned with the health of children of school age, and to have some pension office develop a program of geriatrics, as to have the Department of Labor direct the health program of infants, for, after all, infants are related to labor no closer than through their mothers' recent experiences. The proposal to separate federal health work by age and sex was, therefore, startling; and to many the passage of the Sheppard-Towner Act in 1921 seemed destined to bring to pass what Senator Stanley of Kentucky, in a rip-snorting and somewhat demagogic states-rights speech, earlier in that year, had roared to a Tammany audience: "Babies are to be born by Federal aid and suckled under Federal supervision" (52).

The arguments of the Children's Bureau and its proponents on this bill were somewhat as follows: that the infant mortality and maternal mortality constituted an emergency; that no other government agency had done anything about it; that it was more important to keep the child whole—his home, his play, his psychology, and his health—than to keep the federal health program whole; that maternal and infant health involved welfare, and welfare work was a responsibility of the Children's Bureau, duly delegated to it by Congress in the establishment of the Bureau in 1912.

The hearings on the bill were spirited and to no small extent emotional. The state health officers, and leaders in public health generally, strongly supported a move to have the program developed under the United States Public Health Service as part of its general program. That this Act as introduced was something asked for in the name of labor had no small bearing upon its passage, but perhaps more important than that is the fact that the program advocated by the Children's Bureau caught the attention of the women of the country and, to some extent at least, the maternity and infant division of the Bureau made concrete the woman in public life, in government, in medicine. It was a time when the suffragist movement was approaching a fruitful climax, and the woman in travail and the care of the infant were visualized in all their female attributes. In any event, the Children's Bureau health program was caught up in the feminist movement, and the Sheppard-Towner Act for the Promotion of the Welfare of Maternity and Infancy, under the Department of Labor, became a law November 23, 1921.

The Act authorized an appropriation of $1,240,000 for a period of five years. Of this, $5,000 would go to each state, outright; $5,000 more to each state if matched; the balance, except $50,000 for administration, would be allotted among the states on the basis of population, if the state contributed a similar amount.

The administration of the Act rested with the Children's Bureau, but in a somewhat belated attempt to indicate an interest in co-ordination of federal health activities, Congress provided that there be a Federal Board of Maternity and Infant Hygiene, made up of the Chief of the Children's Bureau, the Surgeon General of the United States Public Health Service, and the United States Commissioner of Education. This was not, however, a policy-forming or regulation-prescribing group, its authority being limited to consideration of the soundness of plans submitted by states requesting federal aid under the Act. Even in this category the Board, under Congressional mandate, must approve any plan if "reasonably appropriate to carry out its [the Act's] purposes."

There was one other provision in the plan which caused those versed in public health administration some concern and was particularly distasteful to state health officers: federal cooperation need not be with the state health department unless that department had in its organization a division of child hygiene or child welfare. The dilemma of the state health departments was that if they did not pretty quickly establish such a division, some other state agency might soon carry on the maternal and child health program. Many state health officers sincerely doubted the wisdom of including in their organizations an administrative division whose sole concern would be the problems of two age groups: women of childbearing age and infants. They foresaw duplications and artificial separations in public health practice, particularly in local health services. The Commonwealth of Massachusetts actually carried its opposition of the Act to the United States Supreme Court, contending that it was federal usurpation of the function of local government, not ceded in the Constitution and therefore in violation of the Tenth Amendment. It is interesting here to note that the Supreme Court disposed of the matter without passing upon the constitutionality of the Act. Instead it ruled the Commonwealth of Massachusetts as without status in the premises.

Between 1922 and 1927 the Division of Maternal and Infant Hygiene carried on an aggressive and productive program. Its professional personnel were essentially women, and in aiding states to obtain directors of maternity and infant hygiene, a much higher proportion of women than men were appointed: the female element in maternal and infant hygiene, and feminine psychology, strongly colored the program. The smugness that existed in many state health organizations was shattered, if not rudely, at least abruptly; precedents, taboos, and sacred relics were brought smashing down; a type of emotionalism, with which male administrators knew not how to cope, arose to plague them. Slovenly programs, and some not so bad, were boldly and openly attacked in one place or another by women's clubs, which seemed not averse to calling names, and giving details.

Perhaps it would be well to interpolate here that this situation is presented not in an attempt to ridicule or deprecate this new feminine element in public health practice. Many might deny that it is an integral element in the support of the Children's Bureau health program. But most unprejudiced observers recognize that it exists. Some fear it, but an increasing number are utilizing it, learning from it, and guiding it for the good of the public health. Even more significant is the fact that all efforts to have the Public Health Service absorb this phase of federal health activity have met with an amazingly effective resistance from the women of the country. Although no survey of federal health activities fails to recommend such an absorption, every recommender is soundly and decisively beaten.

When the period covered by the Sheppard-Towner Act came to a close in 1927 the Act was renewed for two years more, but in 1929 this program ended. Only studies and educational work were carried on from then until 1935 when, under Title V of the Social Security Act, a greatly increased program of maternal and infant hygiene was entrusted to the Children's Bureau. This Act made available to the Children's Bureau the following funds:

Part 1. Maternal and Child Health Services. "For the purpose of enabling each State to extend and improve, as far as practicable under the conditions in such State, services for promoting the health of mothers and children, especially in rural areas and in areas suffering from severe economic distress, there is hereby authorized to be appropriated for each fiscal year, beginning with the fiscal year ending June 30, 1936, the sum of $5,820,000."

From the above sum, for each fiscal year, the Secretary of Labor shall allot to each State, $20,000, and such part of $2,800,000 as he finds that the number of live births in such State bear to the total number of live births in the United States; and also from the total he shall allot to the States $1,980,000 according to the financial need of each State.

Part 2. Services for Crippled Children. "For the purpose of enabling each State to extend and improve (especially in rural areas and in areas suffering from severe economic distress), as far as practicable under the conditions in such State, services for locating crippled children, and for providing medical, surgical, corrective, and other services and care, and facilities for diagnosis, hospitalization, and aftercare, for children who are suffering from conditions which lead to crippling, there is hereby authorized to be appropriated for each fiscal year, beginning with the fiscal year ending June 30, 1936, the sum of $3,870,000."

From the above sum, for each fiscal year, the Secretary of Labor shall allot to each State $20,000 and (a) $1,830,000 to the States, and (b) another $1,000,000 to the States, according to the financial need of each State and after taking into consideration the number of crippled children in such State.

The granting of sums provided under Parts 1 and 2 or part of them, however, is contingent upon the payment of a like amount by the State and its political subdivisions concerned.

In this Act, too, there is a requirement seemingly without precedent, one that introduces still another new element into federal legislation. That part of the Social Security Act relating to the administration of the Child Health Services, Children's Bureau, Department of Labor, sets forth that states are eligible for federal grants-in-aid only if they already have, or rather quickly after 1940 establish, personnel standards on a merit basis for those state employees who might be engaged upon work partly or entirely supported by Title V funds. Whether or not one approves of this depends in part upon his faith in the wisdom of putting a professional organization under Civil Service. But granted that the merits of Civil Service outweigh its demerits, there remains nevertheless the broad, perhaps philosophic, question as to the soundness of attaining an immediate and desirable aim possibly at the expense of a principle. In this instance is a situation where the Federal Government is convinced that Civil Service would be a good thing for the states. The Federal Government cannot force the states to reorganize their internal structure and policies; and it does not try to do this directly. Instead, in this instance it says that a state may have this financial aid only when it has recast this part of its policy. There is no overt action, no pressure, no penalty. The state just doesn't get the money unless it does so and so. Possibly this is one of those instances where the ends justify the means and, since the scheme is beginning to work fairly well and productively, perhaps no question should be raised. However, it is a performance wherein the funds of the Federal Treasury are used to attain ends not un-equivocally set forth in the Constitution and it must be recognized as such in any objective analysis. Parenthetically it may be said that somewhat similar means are utilized by the United States Public Health Service in its grants-in-aid of Social Security funds to states. In this instance the merit system requirement is set forth as a regulation of that Service, and is not contained in the law itself.

The final element for discussion in relation to the programs of the Children's Bureau, Department of Labor, is an activity which was inaugurated as a war measure to continue until six months after the cessation of hostilities. This undertaking is designated as the program for Emergency Maternity and Infant Care for wives of enlisted men in the armed forces. By custom, the title has been shortened to EMIC. Benefits cover women whose husbands are in the four grades of the Army, Navy, Marine Corps, and Coast Guard which receive the lowest pay, and assure to them at government expense, and not as charity but as a right, medical and hospital care in connection with maternity, and similar care of their infants.

This program has grown tremendously and now constitutes one of the great ventures of the Federal Government in public health administration. According to the last available announcement, $29,700,000 is available for the fiscal year 1944, and for 1945, $42,-800,000 (53). This program operates essentially through grants-in-aid to states, in accordance with certain nation-wide policies and procedures of the Children's Bureau.

This method of providing medical care for a segment of the population has aroused considerable controversy, and for that reason has a bearing upon possible future problems in public health practice. There has been no question of the suitability of providing care for wives and infants of men in the armed forces who receive low pay. The controversy has arisen in connection with the administration of the plan. Without attempting to document or specify as to detail, it may be said that some medical organizations object, in principle, to a procedure wherein a third party enters into the relationship between doctor and patient: in this case, where the Federal Government through the state pays the physician for the care of the woman or infant.

Resolutions have been passed by these medical organizations, calling for revision of the regulations, urging that cash allotments be made to the beneficiaries, they in turn to compensate the physician for his services, on the basis of a private arrangement. The Children's Bureau, under what appears to be a mandate of Congress, may make payments only to those rendering service, as physicians and hospitals. As would be expected, and as may be looked for in the future should a federally fostered medical care plan become operative, many other difficulties have arisen which irritate the physicians and hospitals serving, and distress the Bureau administering: standards for qualification, standards of service, fees to specialists as compared to those paid general practitioners, fees for intercurrent illness in pregnancy; the difference between established fees in rural and urban areas; hospital standards and costs of accommodations; the matter of records, applications, reports.

In this controversy, one already prejudiced in either direction could make a good case for his side. Perhaps the attitude of the somewhat official medical organizations, which oppose government payment of the physician, has been adopted not so much because the procedure is inherently wicked as because the whole undertaking represents to them an encroachment of state medicine that has within it potentialities for harm to the private practice of medicine — and some reason for non-concurrence must be found. Just as likely, some of those who administer the plan may appear to physicians in practice as too righteous in their judgments, a shade too smug in their bureaucracy, or to have poor taste in the selection of their hats. In any event the EMIC program represents strikingly one aspect of medicine in a changing order of society and, as such, offers many valuable lessons for the future.

OTHER FEDERAL AGENCIES AND ATTEMPTS TO COORDINATE FEDERAL HEALTH WORK

In the operation of other federal bureaus in the public health field, listed on pages 23–24, there is nothing of significance not already touched upon. Each represents a health activity developed with the health interest secondary to some other and major activity; each exemplifies and contributes to dispersal and, more or less, to lack of coordination of federal health activities; each, but some more than others, has manifested an ability to resist incorporation into the principal health agency of the Federal Government.

The matter of coordinating federal health activities has long been under consideration and every so often a plan is presented to bring this about. General surveys of the Federal Government, made from time to time, invariably include recommendations for regrouping of health activities; and special bills relating to federal public health organization have appeared over the past three quarters of a century. Those vary from laws authorizing executive action in this regard, to bold plans for a National Department of Health with the Secretary a member of the President's Cabinet. Leigh (54) has listed moves of one sort or another, but all aiming at coordination of federal health services, as follows:

1. The Cox plan of 1872 for a bureau of health in the Interior Department. Other isolated bills since that time have made substantially the same proposal—most recently the plan submitted by Secretary Work in 1924 to the Joint Committee on Administrative Re-

organization for the internal reorganization of his department through establishing three main divisions: health, education, and public works and domain.

2. The Bowditch plan of 1875 for a Cabinet department of health, with a commission representing each state, holding annual deliberative sessions.

3. The National Board of Health, 1879–83.

4. The Committee of One Hundred plan for a Cabinet department, 1906–12, introduced at successive sessions by Senator Owen and Senator France.

5. Transfer to, and organization of, a health bureau in the then Department of Commerce and Labor, presented in 1910 by Representative Mann.

6. The Taft Commission on Economy and Efficiency proposal for an independent health service, 1910–12.

7. The Smoot bills for a consolidated health unit under an assistant secretary of the Treasury Department, 1912–15.

8. The Harding-Sawyer-Kenyon proposal of a health unit as one of the four main divisions in a newly established department of public welfare, 1919–21. Substantially the same proposal was made by Mr. John Pratt of the National Budget Committee, 1920–21, and presented to Congress by Senator McCormick, first as a separate measure and a year later as part of a statute providing for general administrative reorganization.

9. The plan of the Joint Committee on Reorganization for public health as one of the three main divisions in a Cabinet department of public welfare, included in its scheme for general administrative reorganization, 1923–25.

10. The W. F. Willoughby plan for a department of public health as an essential element in a proposal for general administrative reorganization, 1921–23.

11. The Tobey proposal for an enlarged health bureau or unit in

the Treasury Department with provision for executive transfer of health agencies thereto and correlation of all health activities, 1926.

Since then other efforts toward coordination have been made, usually under authority granted to the President for reorganization of the executive branch of the government. Mr. Hoover seriously considered this, and for a time it appeared that out of the White House Conference on Child Health and Protection which he called in 1930 some definite action would be taken. That Conference's Committee on Public Health Organization recommended (55) that by Congressional act the health activities of the Children's Bureau, Department of Labor, and the Division of Vital Statistics, Bureau of the Census, Department of Commerce, be transferred to the United States Public Health Service. Subsequent action or lack of action in connection with that part of the proposal relating to the Children's Bureau health program is reflected in a footnote of this Committee's report.

> The recommendation in the majority report of the Committee for the transfer from the Children's Bureau to the Public Health Service of the functions, personnel, and necessary appropriations of the health activities of the Bureau's Divisions of Child Hygiene, and Maternity and Infancy, met with vigorous protest when it was presented to the Conference. President Hoover expressed the wish that this point of controversy be referred to a continuing committee of the Conference. A vote on this recommendation was not taken by the Conference and the Continuation Committee has not thought it desirable to take any action on the subject (55).

The above quotation, in its restraint and mildness, covers the fact that some thirty-two members of this Committee, outstanding in administrative, technical, and educational fields of public health, were completely routed by three dissenting members. One of the latter, the Chief of the Children's Bureau, rested her case upon a conclusion that the needs of the child should be considered as a whole by one government agency and stated that "if it were necessary to choose between efficient organization for promotion of the general health and the most effective method of promoting the health of children, I should consider the latter as of greater importance" (56). The second dissenting opinion was expressed by the Speaker of the House of Delegates, American Medical Association, and the third by the Secretary of the American Medical Association (57). Each of these officers expressed himself as in accord with many of the recommendations of the Committee; both objected to the plan involving federal subsidies of states in their health work.

The above is recounted at some length because it exemplifies the fact that convictions and agreements of those active in the public health field do not necessarily carry weight with legislative bodies or principal executives. In this instance it was not opposition by representatives of the American Medical Association that blocked the proposal; it was the determined and skilful resistance and the display of formidable support by the Chief of the Children's Bureau. As nearly as can be determined, Mr. Hoover was sorry he had ever had the question raised.

There is, too, a more recent instance wherein a detached activity, closely related to public health, was able to maintain its aloofness from the principal federal health agency. Only in 1942 was a bill introduced into Congress providing that the Division of Vital Statistics, Bureau of the Census, Department of Commerce, be transferred to the United States Public Health Service. There were many reasons why this should be done, a few but not very good ones why it should not be done. The provisions of the bill as originally written were not all that could be desired, but there was general agreement that its objective was sound. There seemed no doubt that it would pass. Then, it would appear, some powerful departmental voice spoke and the bill died in committee.

From time to time the American Medical Association has passed resolutions as to a National Department of Health. That organization has not, however, conducted any vigorous or continuing program to this end, nor has it indicated itself to be entirely selfless and unprejudiced in this matter, in that it has set forth that the proposed Secretary of Health must be a physician and a member of his county medical society (58).

Most unprejudiced students of government agree that it is unlikely that Congress will, in the foreseeable future, authorize departmental status for federal health activities. Departments, in the executive branch of the United States Government, are rather vast things, purposely limited in number; and just as good a case could be made for many other special interests as for health. The principal advantage, from the public health standpoint, would be the influence of a political figure of the stature of a Secretary. Public health has not had many politically powerful voices speak in its favor, and its championing by a vigorous leader in the executive branch would be helpful. It seems, though, that even if there were a Secretary of Health, the disadvantages of having this person a doctor of medicine might outweigh the advantages. He could not function politically on a Secretarial level and remain competent in the medical and public health field or vice versa.

REFERENCES

1. Journal of the Clerk of the House of Representatives, 1792, pp. 94, 95, 96. An unsuccessful search was made for the Memorial of the Marine Society of Boston, and for documents of the Marine Hospital at Washington, Va.
2. Act of July 16, 1798 (1 Stat. L. 605–606, Ch. 77). An Act for the relief of sick and disabled Seamen.
   Not infrequently, it is said that this bill authorized the President "to nominate and appoint medical officers" (Public Health Reports, 36:1165, May 27, 1921). Strictly speaking, this is not correct. The terms "medical officer" and "physician" do not appear in the bill. The President was "authorized to nominate and appoint one or more persons to be called . . .

directors of the marine hospital of the United States. . . ." It was not required, nor was it prohibited, that they be physicians.

3. Falk, I. S. Administrative Medicine, Haven Emerson, *ed.*, pt. III, p. 759.
New York: Thomas Nelson and Son, 1941.

Falk has compressed matters somewhat in this statement. Actually,
provision for care of Navy personnel was not included in the original bill
but in the 1799 version (1 U.S. Stat. L. 729), nor did the original contain
any reference to support of this medical service by general taxation, although this was inferred in legislative discussions. Appropriations were
later made, however, to meet deficiencies or to provide specifically for
building of hospitals. Finally, support of this work for merchant seamen
and certain other government employees was transferred completely to
funds derived from general taxation.

4. Terris, Milton. An Early System of Compulsory Health Insurance in the
United States, 1798–1884. Bulletin of the History of Medicine, 15:5, 433–
444, May 1944.

5. House of Representatives, Sick and Disabled Seamen. Annals of Congress,
April 1798, pp. 1386–1394. Text of the bill is found on pages 3787–3789.

6. First Annual Report of the Supervising Surgeon of the Marine Hospital
Service of the United States. Washington: Government Printing Office,
1872.

7. Act of February 26, 1811 (2 Stat. L. 650, Ch. 26). An Act establishing
Navy Hospitals.

8. Leigh, Robert D. Federal Health Administration in the United States.
New York: Harper and Bros., 1927, p. 83.

9. Annual Report of the Supervising Surgeon of the Marine-Hospital Service. Washington: Government Printing Office, 1882, p. 40.

10. Leigh, Robert D., *op. cit.*, pp. 90, 91.

11. First Annual Report of the Supervising Surgeon of the Marine Hospital
Service of the United States. Washington: Government Printing Office,
1872, pp. 10, 11.

12. Leigh, Robert D., *op. cit.*, p. 92.

13. Act of June 29, 1870 (16 Stat. L. 169, Ch. 169). An Act to reorganize the
Marine Hospital Service, and to provide for the relief of sick and disabled
Seamen.

14. The Congressional Globe, 41st Congress, February 21, 1870, pp. 1450–
1453.

Although this provision that a medical officer of the Army or Navy
might be detailed to the Marine Hospital Service was eliminated from this
bill, a custom somewhat in reversal of this is now current, in that the
President may detail Public Health Service officers to either the Army or
Navy. There is further provision that Public Health Service officers may be
detailed to direct certain health activities in other branches of the Federal
Government. This makes for more coordination of federal health activities
than might be apparent at first glance.

15. Annual Report of the Supervising Surgeon of the Marine-Hospital Service of the United States. Washington: Government Printing Office, 1873, pp. 16, 17.

16. Annual Report of the Supervising Surgeon of the Marine-Hospital Service of the United States. Washington: Government Printing Office, 1874, p. 14.

17. Act of June 26, 1884 (23 Stat. L. 53, Ch. 121). An Act to remove certain burdens on the American merchant marine and encourage the American foreign carrying trade, and for other purposes.

18. Act of March 3, 1905 (33 Stat. L. 1217, Ch. 1484). An Act making appropriations to supply deficiencies in the appropriations for the fiscal year ending June 30, 1905, and for prior years, and for other purposes.

19. First Annual Report of the Supervising Surgeon of the Marine Hospital Service of the United States. Washington: Government Printing Office, 1872, p. 26.

20. Annual Reports of the United States Public Health Service, 1941–42, 1942–43. Washington: Government Printing Office, 1943, Table 13, p. 181.

21. First Annual Report of the Supervising Surgeon of the Marine Hospital Service of the United States. Washington: Government Printing Office, 1872, p. 89.

22. Annual Reports of the United States Public Health Service, 1941–42, 1942–43. Washington: Government Printing Office, 1943, Table 13, p. 181.

    Figure for total expenditures from *ibid.*, Table 1, p. 162. The item as to cost per patient day under 1943 is for the year 1941, which is the last year for which this figure is available, and is from the Annual Report of the Surgeon General, United States Public Health Service, 1941, p. 110.

23. Act of July 20, 1790 (1 Stat. L. 131, Ch. 29). An Act for the government and regulation of Seamen in the merchants service.

24. Act of April 3, 1794 (1 Stat. L. 353, Ch. 17). An Act to authorize the President of the United States in certain cases to alter the place for holding a session of Congress.

25. Hearings before a Subcommittee of the Committee on Interstate and Foreign Commerce, House of Representatives, 78th Congress, 2nd Session, on H. R. 3379. A bill to codify the laws relating to the Public Health Service, and for other purposes. Washington, March 1, 2, 3, 7, 8, 9, 10, and 14, 1944.

26. Act of May 27, 1796 (1 Stat. L. 474, Ch. 31). An Act relative to quarantine.

27. Jones, Joseph. Medical and Surgical Memoirs. New Orleans: Printed for the author by L. Graham and Son, 1890, vol. III, pt. 1, p. 11.

28. 118 U.S. 455: Morgan's Steamship Company vs. Louisiana Board of Health. May 10, 1886, decided.

29. Act of April 29, 1878 (20 Stat. L. 37, Ch. 66). An Act to prevent the introduction of contagious or infectious diseases into the United States.

30. Act of March 3, 1879 (20 Stat. L. 484, Ch. 202). An Act to prevent the introduction of infectious or contagious diseases into the United States, and to establish a National Board of Health.

31. Jones, Joseph, *op. cit.*, pt. 2, p. 299.

32. Act of February 15, 1893 (27 Stat. L. 449, Ch. 114). An Act granting additional quarantine powers and imposing additional duties upon the Marine-Hospital Service.

33. Act of March 27, 1890 (26 Stat. L. 31, Ch. 51). An Act to prevent the introduction of contagious diseases from one State to another and for the punishment of certain offenses.

34. Act of July 1, 1902 (32 Stat. L. 712, Ch. 1370, Sec. 7). An Act to increase the efficiency and change the name of the United States Marine-Hospital Service.

35. Act of July 1, 1902 (32 Stat. L. 728, Ch. 1378). An Act to regulate the sale of viruses, serums, toxins, and analogous products in the District of Columbia, to regulate interstate traffic in said articles, and for other purposes.

36. Cabell, J. L. Annual Address (as President). Papers and Reports of the American Public Health Association, 5:1–23, 1879. Boston: Houghton Mifflin and Company, 1880.

37. Act of August 14, 1912 (37 Stat. L. 309, Ch. 288). An Act to change the name of the Public Health and Marine-Hospital Service to the Public Health Service, to increase the pay of officers of said service, and for other purposes.

38. Act of February 28, 1916 (39 Stat. L. 21, Ch. 37). An Act making appropriations to supply further urgent deficiencies in appropriations for the fiscal year ending June 30, 1916, and prior years, and for other purposes.

39. Ferrell, John A., and Mead, Pauline A. History of County Health Organizations in the United States, 1908–1933. Washington: Government Printing Office, 1936, p. 5 (Public Health Bulletin No. 222).

40. Act of August 14, 1935 (49 Stat. L. 620, Ch. 531). An Act to provide for the general welfare by establishing a system of Federal old-age benefits, and by enabling the several States to make more adequate provision for aged persons, blind persons, dependents and crippled children, maternal and child welfare, public health, and the administration of their unemployment compensation laws; to establish a Social Security Board; to raise revenue; and for other purposes.

41. Rules and Regulations of the Public Health Service. Basis of allotment and Rules and Regulations of the Surgeon General governing payments to states under Title VI of the Social Security Act as amended for the fiscal year 1943 and each year thereafter. (As amended November 13, 1943.)

42. Act of July 9, 1918 (40 Stat. L. 886, Ch. 143). An Act making appropriations for the support of the Army for the fiscal year ending June 30, 1919.

43. Act of May 24, 1938 (52 Stat. L. 439, Ch. 267). An Act to impose addi-

tional duties upon the United States Public Health Service in connection with the investigation and control of venereal disease. (Of funds available, a certain proportion is utilized for Public Health Service activities, and the balance is distributed to the states on the following basis: Population, 17.93; extent of venereal problem, 42.18; financial needs, 17.67.)

44. Act of July 1, 1944 (Public Law 410: Ch. 373). The Public Health Service Act.

This was an Act to codify all laws relating to the Public Health Service, and since it is now in effect, all legal references should relate to this Act. However, for historical purposes and to indicate sequences and developments, references in this monograph are to the original acts concerned.

45. S. 1161, 78th Congress, 1st Session. The 78th Congress failed to act upon this proposed legislation.

46. Reorganization plan, submitted to Congress by the President April 25, 1939, under authority of the Reorganization Act of 1939 (Public Law 19: 76th Congress) became effective July 1, 1939.

47. Act of November 11, 1943 (Public Law 184: 78th Congress). An Act relating to the organization and functions of the Public Health Service, and for other purposes.

48. Schmeckebier, Laurence F. The Public Health Service. Baltimore: Johns Hopkins Press, 1923, p. 46. (Service Monograph of the United States Government No. 10.)

49. Act of April 9, 1912 (37 Stat. L. 79, Ch. 73). An Act to establish in the Department of Commerce and Labor a bureau to be known as the Children's Bureau.

50. H. R. 12634, 65th Congress, 2nd Session.

51. Act of November 23, 1921 (42 Stat. L. 224, Ch. 135). An Act for the promotion of the welfare and hygiene of maternity and infancy, and for other purposes. The appropriation was for a five-year period ending June 30, 1927.

52. Leigh, Robert D., op. cit., p. 430.

53. Children's Bureau. History and Functions of the Children's Bureau. Washington: United States Department of Labor, September 1, 1944, p. 8.

54. Leigh, Robert D., op. cit., pp. 498–499.

55. Public Health Organization: Section II—Public Health Service and Administration. Report of the Committee on Public Health Organization, White House Conference on Child Health and Protection. New York: The Century Company, 1932, p. 209.

56. Ibid., p. 337.

57. Ibid., p. 338.

58. Report of Reference Committee on Legislation and Public Relations of the House of Delegates (American Medical Association), June 8, 1943, Resolution 3. Journal of the American Medical Association, 122:621, June 26, 1943.

III

STATE HEALTH DEPARTMENTS

Aʟᴛʜᴏᴜɢʜ the state health department is the agency in which resides the greatest public health power, as compared with local and federal, discussion of this phase of the subject must be rather brief, for the organizational and functional structure of state health agencies is already fairly well defined in all states, and whether it should be so or not, the situation is to some extent static. In contrast, there are gaps and deficiencies in local health departments where most health service is rendered; and in the Federal Government, the situation is everything but static: great forces are stirring, and from these new pressures and resources may come.

There are, however, certain features of public health work, inherent in the state as a once sovereign entity, that it is advantageous to pick up and pursue from the past to the present time. In undertaking to do this it must be remembered that the evolution of state public health service is the outcome of forty-eight different developments. One may not, therefore, assume that the same problems have been and are common to all state health departments or that public health practice is the same in all states. But with these reservations, it may be said that there are certain similarities in state health organization and administration, and the factors that have influenced the development of health services in the different states have at least the shadow of a common denominator.

In an attempt to analyze the development of state health services or to determine the significance of their development, one must keep in mind two important and essential facts. The first of these is that in the establishment of the Constitution of the United States the individual states did not cede to the Federal Government the responsibility and authority for the preservation of health within their respective borders. They therefore retained this function, and, regardless of how well they have acquitted themselves, have theoretically remained responsible for all health activities other than those in which interstate and international responsibilities are involved. The second point of importance is that so far as concerns measures for protection of the public health, local action preceded state-wide programs. The explanation of this is not difficult to find. Formerly, public health measures were instituted only to meet some situation that had already developed, as an epidemic or an ill-smelling nuisance. The state as a whole did not smell the odor of a local slaughterhouse. Legislatures were preoccupied with the maintenance of order and the encouragement of trade, and not at all interested in the formulation of aggressive and far-flung social and health programs. It was, therefore, about three generations after the establishment of the first local boards of health that state boards of health came into existence.

It would appear that state authorities took cognizance of health problems only when there was pressure from a comparatively large number of localities which shared a common problem or when some powerful local jurisdiction, such as a large city, demanded state action. The type of problem which precipitated action appears in most instances to have been the epidemic. Thus yellow fever was probably responsible for the creation of the first state board of health in the United States, when Louisiana established such a board in 1855. The port of New Orleans, perhaps more than any other, had suffered recurrent waves of this disease, and that experience loomed sufficiently large in Louisiana affairs to obtain state action. The records as to the subsequent history of this first board of health of Louisiana are not full and clear. It would seem, however, that having been born in the fear of an epidemic it became quiescent and practically non-existent, and some forty-three years afterwards was revitalized and reorganized.

Yellow fever also led to the appointment of what was in effect the first "state health officer" of record when, in 1712, the General Assembly of Carolina appointed Gilbert Guttery as health officer, imposing upon him the duty of inquiring into the state of health of all persons who might come into the province aboard any ship or vessel. He was to board vessels, study the records of the ship and the health of the passengers and, when indicated, send persons to a designated pesthouse, and otherwise to take such measures as he deemed necessary. Various penalties were imposed on those who might violate the provisions of the Act. Further, he was required to change his clothes and cleanse himself before returning ashore should he find sickness on any ship inspected. The sicknesses specified were "Plague, Smal Pox, Spotted Feavour, Siam distemper, Guinea feavour, or aney other Malignant Contagious Disease." The Act itself was repealed by an Act of September, 1721. The first page of the Act of 1712 is reproduced as a frontispiece (1). The full text is reprinted in the Appendix, pages 201–208.

The first state board of health that remained effectively in existence from the time of its original organization was that of Massachusetts. It was established in 1869. The inception of this board was somewhat different from that of Louisiana, although recurring epidemics undoubtedly played a part in its origin. But more important than these problems is the fact that there came into the public health field in Massachusetts, about one hundred years ago, the first public health statesman of America, one Lemuel Shattuck. Shattuck represented in the state field what Woodworth represented in the federal area: a strong and wise personality. His ideas and contributions are of sufficient importance and significance to justify further consideration of them.

Shattuck was not a physician. Actually he was a publisher with a fine mind and a broad interest in human affairs. He had been greatly interested in the work and writings of Chadwick in England, and through a fortunate chain of circumstances was, in 1849, appointed Chairman of the Massachusetts Sanitary Commission which the Governor had been authorized by the legislature to appoint for the purpose of undertaking a sanitary survey of the state.

The report of this commission was presented in 1850 and has become a classic in public health literature and documents. This report "contained an outline of a state system of public health administration so comprehensive that even today it may well serve as an ideal for future realization" (2). It recommended that the public health laws of the state be revised and improved and that a general board of health be established; that the board, as far as practicable, be composed of two physicians, one counselor at law, one chemist or natural philosopher, one civil engineer, and two persons of other professions or occupations.

Shattuck did not believe that the members of the board should be selected exclusively from one profession, for reasons which are pertinent today as then, and are as follows:

1. Numerous questions, requiring a knowledge possessed by different professions, will be presented for discussion and decision; and it is desirable that the Board should be able to bring competent knowledge to the investigation of every subject.

2. To show to all that the promotion of public health is a matter which does not belong exclusively to the medical profession, but concerns every profession and every person. The idea which too generally prevails, that everything relating to health belongs to one profession, operates against sanitary improvement. The services of medical men are indispensable; but the services of other professions, and of every person in their respective spheres, must be put in requisition, before reform can be complete (3).

Amazing for that day and age, the Shattuck report recommended that the board be authorized to appoint a full-time secretary who would be paid a proper salary for his services. The report went further into detail as to the data to be gathered in a sanitary survey and set forth suggestions for action designed to cover a wide range of public health services: housing, schools, streets, water, excreta disposal, vital statistics, vaccination, tuberculosis, nuisances, inquests, the insane, cemeteries, quarantine of pestilence, public bathing houses, smoke nuisance, patent medicines and nostrums, adulterated food, drink, and medicine; the formation of sanitary associations, of institutions to educate and qualify females to be nurses for the sick; that persons be specially educated in sanitary science; that physicians keep records of cases professionally attended; that clergymen make public health a subject of one or more discourses annually; that each family keep records of the physical and sanitary condition of its members; that there be parental education in the care of children; and finally, that "individuals make frequent sanitary examinations of themselves and endeavor to promote personal health and prevent disease."

Shattuck's recommendations seem to have been forgotten for some years after the report was submitted, but finally came to partial fruition in the organization of the state board of health some fifteen years later. Here occurred one of those ironies in which public health is replete, illustrating that sound technical advice does not necessarily survive political debate and expediency. Perhaps it should not. In any event, in spite of the fact that what might be called the keystone of Shattuck's recommendation was vital statistics, Massachusetts is now the only state in the Union in which this activity is not a function of the state health organization.

Health Work in the State Carried by Agencies Other Than the State Health Department

Before turning to consideration of the structure and functions of state health departments, it would seem wise to consider the kind and amount of health work that is carried on under state direction but not immediately as a part of the program of the state health department itself. The degree to which state agencies, other than health departments, participate in public health work varies from state to state; and the kind of health activity carried on by an extra-health department agency is not necessarily the same in one state as in another. For this reason, no single list of health activities carried on by state agencies other than health departments would be applicable to all states, but the tables and discussion presented below will indicate the situation in general.

Mountin and Flook (4), in their recent study of public health activities carried on by states, collected information on 35 separate categories within and outside the program of state health departments. These were as follows: vital statistics, acute communicable disease control, tuberculosis control (prevention and treatment—including hospitalization), maternity hygiene, venereal disease control, infant and preschool hygiene, school health services, industrial hygiene, workingmen's compensation, sanitation of water supplies and sewage disposal facilities, housing control, plumbing control, smoke, fumes, and odors control, rodent control, garbage collection and disposal, shellfish sanitation, milk sanitation, malaria control, pest mosquito control, supervision of hotels, restaurants, tourist camps, and other facilities for the traveling public, food and drug control, mental hygiene (prevention and treatment—including hospitalization), care of crippled children, cancer control, prevention and care of blindness, vocational rehabilitation, pneumonia control, hookworm control, health services for migratory labor, general medical care of the needy, dental services, laboratory services, health education, research activities, licensure of professions and agencies significant in relation to the public health.

The same authors report that in one state "as many as 18 separate agencies contribute something to the health activities covered." They continue:

TABLE II. Approximate total and per capita annual expenditures* by all official state agencies for health activities, and proportion of the total amount which was expended by agencies of each specified type (5)

State or territory	Approximate annual expenditure* by all official state agencies for health activities		Per cent of total** expended by each agency								
	Total	Per Capita	Health department	Special boards or commissions	Department of welfare	Board of control	Independent state hospitals, laboratories, etc.	Department of labor	State university or college	Department of agriculture	All other agencies of state government
Total	$285,715,800	$1.90	18.5	25.0	21.3	16.0	5.4	3.2	3.2	2.3	5.1
Alabama	2,668,900	.94	42.9	45.2	(a)				1.1	2.9	7.9
Arizona	1,130,500	2.26	15.6	34.3	14.0	30.6	1.0				4.5
Arkansas	2,721,000	1.40	23.6	23.9	8.7	33.4			8.5		1.9
California	14,096,400	2.04	17.4		.2	49.9		20.4	7.2	1.6	3.3
Colorado	2,752,600	2.45	16.8	.5	13.1		42.0		23.1	.3	4.2
Connecticut	6,007,200	3.51	9.3	31.1	1.5		49.3	1.2	(a)		7.6
Delaware	1,076,100	4.04	41.7	(a)	(a)		55.2	(a)			3.1
District of Col.	6,608,800	10.44	40.2	1.4							58.4
Florida	3,109,900	1.64	17.7	22.0	(a)	53.1				3.8	3.4
Georgia	2,964,200	.95	38.7	(a)	55.4				.8	4.9	.2
Idaho	986,000	1.88	25.7	b 23.3	37.1					12.2	1.7
Illinois	17,678,000	2.24	8.7	.2	c 80.0			1.2	(d)	4.6	5.3
Indiana	7,332,800	2.14	9.1	1.6	76.4			(a)	10.2		2.7
Iowa	4,780,300	1.88	10.0	b .4	b .4	47.9		.2	34.0	4.7	2.4
Kansas	3,008,400	1.67	13.5	9.7	72.2			.8	(a)	1.0	2.8
Kentucky	2,522,500	.89	40.1	8.6	47.3			(a)			4.0
Louisiana	5,754,200	2.43	17.9	3.5	(a)		76.2	0.1			2.3
Maine	2,023,900	2.39	18.3	.5	b 9.5	61.7		(a)		7.8	2.2
Maryland	4,102,000	2.25	18.6	48.5	.1		.7	.8	15.9	.5	14.9
Massachusetts	13,781,200	3.19	27.5	52.2	b 12.8			1.4		3.3	2.8
Michigan	12,439,100	2.37	10.5	80.4	b .2			(e b)	6.2	1.5	1.2
Minnesota	6,148,500	2.20	11.3	2.4	60.5			.7	15.5	1.4	4.3
Mississippi	2,143,900	.98	42.4	b 11.6	.5	41.2				(d)	4.3
Missouri	5,058,400	1.34	14.2	(a)	.1	79.3		.6	2.7	.8	2.8
Montana	1,472,700	2.63	11.4	25.9	11.7	46.9				1.9	2.2
Nebraska	1,724,700	1.31	9.1	(a)		82.3		.9		7.7	
Nevada	469,200	4.26	21.9	51.3		17.9			1.8	1.6	5.5
New Hampshire	1,637,400	3.33	12.7	8.9	9.5		61.5	.6		5.1	1.7
New Jersey	10,875,900	2.61	8.3	3.4	6.7	76.8		1.5		1.3	2.0
New Mexico	690,000	1.30	32.2	(a)	b 19.0		40.8				8.0
New York	44,054,800	3.27	15.9	78.6	(a)			2.1		b 1.6	1.3
North Carolina	3,260,400	.91	36.3	14.1	.6		45.1	.1		b 1.6	2.2
North Dakota	2,090,900	3.26	8.4	13.3	16.4	56.5	2.8			1.0	1.6
Ohio	12,932,800	1.87	7.2	31.1	51.2			1.9	b 3.6	1.7	3.3
Oklahoma	3,470,300	1.49	15.6	6.0	(f)	54.8		.4	20.4	(a)	2.8
Oregon	3,119,600	2.86	9.1	b 33.8	b 3.7	45.7		1.1	b 1.4	2.9	2.8
Pennsylvania	26,098,000	2.64	14.2	1.0	65.2			12.4		4.9	2.3
Rhode Island	2,355,300	3.30	33.7	1.4	60.2			.9		2.1	1.7
South Carolina	3,523,800	1.85	25.1	(a)			71.9	.9	1.2	(a)	.9
South Dakota	1,359,400	2.11	15.1	2.6	13.4	62.9		(d)	1.9	2.0	2.1
Tennessee	2,228,500	.76	50.8	(a)	(a)	44.2		(d)	(a)	b 2.2	2.8
Texas	5,512,600	.86	20.5	(a)	(a)	70.3		(a)		3.4	9.5
Utah	1,401,400	2.55	31.8	28.1	.9		34.4			3.4	1.4
Vermont	889,700	2.48	20.4	16.4	57.3			.5	(a)	3.8	2.1
Virginia	4,392,700	1.64	42.6	b 52.5	2.7					1.4	
Washington	3,818,900	2.20	7.5	b .1	b 2.6			1.3	b 20.2	4.3	65.5
West Virginia	3,781,600	1.99	10.4	17.8	21.9	39.1				1.7	7.8
Wisconsin	7,092,400	2.26	9.1	1.7	2.9	g 60.2			17.0	5.5	3.0
Wyoming	569,500	2.27	19.2	22.7		48.9		.9		2.0	6.3
Alaska	182,900	2.51	93.6		(a)						6.4
Hawaii	2,129,900	5.03	52.4		2.3	19.9	22.6				2.8
Puerto Rico	3,534,200	1.89	99.2	.8				(a)			3.6
Virgin Islands	151,500	6.09	96.4		(a)						

In no jurisdiction are less than 6 agencies involved, and the median number of departments, boards, and commissions concerned with programs having public health significance is 11 per State. When dispersion is viewed from the point of specific activity among all the States, the situation is quite as remarkable. Records for a few activities are cited. For the Nation as a whole, 15 different types of State organizations participate in food and drug control work; 11 are engaged in sanitation of water supplies; 11 touch upon the problem of general medical care of the needy. The latter statement, by the way, represents only about three-fourths of the areas included because 14 States make no provision for service of this type. Hospitalization of the tuberculous is the product of 9 different types of State agencies and hospitalization of mental patients, of 7. Mental hygiene, a relatively new entrant into public health awareness, is split among 9 separate organizations in the 17 States which have initiated such activities.

The approximate amounts that each state agency expends in certain major lines of public health activities are shown in Table II and the source of these funds is shown in Table III. Similarly, the number of persons employed in this wide range of health activities by various state agencies is shown in Table IV.

From the data presented in these tables it should be noted that the total expenditure by agencies of state government, without regard to sources of funds, was $285,715,800 as of 1940; that the average expenditure per state was $1.90 per capita, the median $2.20.

---

* Expenditures for the health services considered represent index rather than absolute amounts. Because of variations in fiscal practices, figures cover the most recent year for which information was available at the date of interview. In some instances, estimates were accepted in the absence of precise expenditure records; in others, it was impossible to secure even an estimate.
** Percentage distribution is based upon the expenditure information reported for each agency even though that amount might be incomplete.
 a Information not available.   b Information incomplete.
 c Represents expenditures of two separate agencies of this classification.
 d Units of the University of Illinois rendering service included here operate jointly with the department of welfare and are financed by that agency.   e Less than one-tenth of 1 per cent.
 f Financial grant-in-aid to the crippled children's commission for administration. Figure included in expenditure of that agency.
 g The board of control no longer functions in Wisconsin. Operation of tuberculosis hospitals has been transferred to the state health department and operation of mental hospitals is now a function of the department of public welfare. However, records for a complete fiscal year were not available under the new administrative set-up.

TABLE III. Approximate total and per capita annual expenditures* by all official state agencies for health activities, and proportion of the total amount which was derived from each specified source (6)

State or territory	Approximate total annual expenditure* by all official state agencies for health activities	Approximate per capita annual expenditure* by all official state agencies for health activities	Per cent of total derived from each source					
			State	Local *	U. S. Public Health Service Title VI	U. S. Public Health Service V.D. funds	U. S. Children's Bureau Title V	Other
Total	$285,715,800	$1.90	81.4	3.9	3.2	1.0	2.5	8.0
Alabama	2,668,900	.94	66.6		11.0	5.3	8.9	8.2
Arizona	1,130,500	2.26	53.8		4.9	1.2	8.3	31.8
Arkansas	2,721,000	1.40	80.4		8.2	3.7	5.5	2.2
California	14,096,400	2.04	62.7	7.9	2.2	1.2	1.8	24.2
Colorado	2,752,600	2.45	62.2	9.3	4.5	1.2	4.8	18.0
Connecticut	6,007,200	3.51	72.6	13.0	1.7	.4	1.2	11.1
Delaware	1,076,100	4.04	83.1		4.0	.5	4.6	7.8
District of Columbia	6,608,800	10.44	97.3		1.0	.1	1.6	
Florida	3,109,900	1.64	73.7	3.4	4.4	1.0	4.4	13.1
Georgia	2,964,200	.95	78.8	.1	9.9	2.0	7.1	2.1
Idaho	986,000	1.88	49.3	2.1	7.4	1.4	7.0	32.8
Illinois	17,678,000	2.24	93.9		2.4	.6	1.9	1.2
Indiana	7,332,800	2.14	93.4	1.7	2.7	.7	1.5	
Iowa	4,780,300	1.88	49.6	31.5	3.8	.9	2.4	11.8
Kansas	3,008,400	1.67	74.3	4.7	4.5	1.8	4.2	10.5
Kentucky	2,522,500	.89	75.3		9.0	2.2	7.4	6.1
Louisiana	5,754,200	2.43	93.8		3.0	.6	1.7	.9
Maine	2,023,900	2.39	85.0	1.0	3.2	.4	4.5	5.9
Maryland	4,102,000	2.25	72.9	.8	3.2	.6	4.1	18.4
Massachusetts	13,781,200	3.19	95.7		1.6	.4	1.3	1.0
Michigan	12,439,100	2.37	87.3	6.1	2.2	.9	1.4	2.1
Minnesota	6,148,500	2.20	73.5	11.4	3.2	.5	2.4	9.0
Mississippi	2,143,900	.98	75.8		10.0	4.3	6.5	3.4
Missouri	5,058,400	1.34	88.7	.7	5.4	1.5	2.1	1.6
Montana	1,472,700	2.63	53.2	6.3	3.9	.2	5.6	30.8
Nebraska	1,724,700	1.31	72.2	9.7	3.3	.5	4.4	9.9
Nevada	469,200	4.26	31.3	2.3	6.7	.7	7.0	52.0
New Hampshire	1,637,400	3.33	84.5	.9	3.1	.7	3.4	7.4
New Jersey	10,875,900	2.61	67.2	23.1	1.9	.6	1.8	5.4
New Mexico	690,000	1.30	64.0		10.4	1.3	17.5	6.8
New York	44,054,800	3.27	97.6		1.3	.4	.7	(a)
North Carolina	3,260,400	.91	68.0		9.6	1.6	7.3	13.5
North Dakota	2,090,900	3.26	30.7	47.2	2.9	.1	4.8	14.3
Ohio	12,932,800	1.87	63.2	.3	2.4	1.0	1.5	31.6
Oklahoma	3,470,300	1.49	82.7	2.7	5.4	2.6	3.3	3.3
Oregon	3,119,600	2.86	58.2		2.9	1.0	4.1	33.8
Pennsylvania	26,098,000	2.64	85.9		1.5	.5	1.1	11.0
Rhode Island	2,355,300	3.30	93.2		2.3	.4	2.2	1.9
South Carolina	3,523,800	1.85	87.0	.6	5.5	1.5	4.5	.9
South Dakota	1,359,400	2.11	77.4		5.4	.5	5.0	11.7
Tennessee	2,228,500	.76	63.4	4.6	13.6	3.0	7.6	7.8
Texas	5,512,600	.86	80.6		7.6	4.7	6.4	.7
Utah	1,401,400	2.55	58.9	2.5	4.8	1.0	6.2	26.6
Vermont	889,700	2.48	85.8	.7	4.8	.1	6.1	2.5
Virginia	4,392,700	1.64	81.0	7.0	5.8	2.4	3.6	.2
Washington	3,818,900	2.20	73.0	.6	2.8	1.1	2.2	20.3
West Virginia	3,781,600	1.99	73.0	.5	3.9	.6	3.2	18.8
Wisconsin	7,092,400	2.26	71.9	17.0	2.3	.3	1.9	6.6
Wyoming	569,500	2.27	67.5	(a)	4.8	.3	7.0	20.4
Alaska	182,900	2.51	22.6	13.4	22.2	1.1	38.1	2.6
Hawaii	2,129,900	5.03	91.9	.5	2.7	.6	2.9	1.4
Puerto Rico	3,534,200	1.89	81.8		7.4	3.4	7.4	
Virgin Islands	151,500	6.09	86.1		11.4	2.5		

* Expenditures for the health services considered represent index rather than absolute amounts. Because of variations in fiscal practices, figures cover the most recent year for which information was available at the date of interview. In some instances, because of overlapping and interweaving of activities, estimates were accepted in the absence of precise expenditure records; in others, it was impossible to secure even an estimate.

a Less than one-tenth of 1 per cent.

TABLE IV. Full-time administrative and field personnel employed by official state agencies of different types for health activities (7)

Number of persons employed full time for health work by state agencies of each type

State or territory	All agencies of state government	Health department	Special boards or commissions	Department of welfare	Board of control	Independent state hospitals, laboratories, etc.	Department of labor	State university or college	Department of agriculture	All other agencies of state government
Total	18,737	11,269	1,070	617	106	80	1,086	90	1,496	2,923
Alabama	313	232	7	(a)			15		33	26
Arizona	77	31	7	13	(a)	11				15
Arkansas	98	67	4	17	(a)			(a)		10
California	637	374		12	(a)		88	(a)	57	106
Colorado	160	110	8	2	(a)			(a)	(a)	40
Connecticut	282	174	65	(a)		(a)	30			13
Delaware	97	64	(a)	(a)		(a)	(a)			33
District of Col.	1,864	302	77							1,485
Florida	279	195	77	(a)	5				(a)	2
Georgia	294	195	(a)	17			7		(a)	2
Idaho	46	36	(a)	2					5	3
Illinois	1,012	480	8	131			75	(a)	170	148
Indiana	398	223	30	49			15	(a)		81
Iowa	288	168	(a)	11	3		3	(a)	56	47
Kansas	162	95	31	7			11	(a)	11	7
Kentucky	231	187	7	6			(a)			31
Louisiana	559	470	12	(a)		34	2			41
Maine	159	127	3	(a)	4		(a)		18	7
Maryland	178	135	6	2		(a)	19	(a)	12	4
Massachusetts	893	420	146	(a)			71		99	157
Michigan	555	377	41	8			3	(a)	69	57
Minnesota	470	272	32	70			26	7	37	26
Mississippi	140	123	4	3	(a)					10
Missouri	309	230	3	2	12		11	11	(a)	10
Montana	76	43	14	5	1				13	
Nebraska	102	55	(a)		7		6		34	
Nevada	58	35	(a)		3			5	11	4
New Hampshire	96	70	6	(a)		(a)	4		15	1
New Jersey	548	315	61	(a)	25		88		18	41
New Mexico	65	51		11		(a)				3
New York	1,973	1,282	103	12			358		174	44
North Carolina	203	185	(a)	5		(a)	1		12	(a)
North Dakota	106	53	4	14	(a)	22			7	6
Ohio	470	153	87	70			(a)	(a)	54	106
Oklahoma	208	132	26	(a)	26		11	(a)	(a)	13
Oregon	157	60	15	10	1		12	4	35	20
Pennsylvania	1,587	1,013	79	23			162		208	102
Rhode Island	170	118	15	16			5		16	
South Carolina	157	126	2	(a)	(a)		16	13	(a)	(a)
South Dakota	80	41	5	(a)	(a)			17	11	6
Tennessee	321	284	(a)	(a)	(a)		(a)	(a)	21	16
Texas	376	351	(a)	(a)	3		(a)			22
Utah	154	130	9	1		(a)				14
Vermont	100	74	15	(a)					8	3
Virginia	433	392	8	6			8	(a)	17	2
Washington	177	64	1	12			27		59	14
West Virginia	236	81	1	49	14		9		24	58
Wisconsin	415	201	35	22	(b)				33	102 · 22
Wyoming	55	34	6			2	3		3	7
Alaska	31	28		(a)						3
Hawaii	314	261		9	(a)	13				31
Puerto Rico	508	498	10	(a)				(a)		
Virgin Islands	60	52		(a)						8

a Part-time or institutional personnel only.

b The board of control no longer functions in Wisconsin. Operation of tuberculosis hospitals has been transferred to the state health department and operation of mental hospitals is now a function of the department of public welfare. However, records for a complete fiscal year were not available under the new administrative set-up.

The lowest per capita per year was found in Tennessee, $0.76, and the highest in Nevada, $4.26.

This high and low per capita expenditure by the state as a whole for all health purposes is not, however, a true index of what the state may be doing in public health work. A number of other factors must be taken into consideration. Important among these is the amount of health work done by central state agencies and that done locally. Data in Table V (page 107) indicate this to some extent in relation to each state. Also to be considered is how much of this total expenditure for all health or health-related activities is spent by the state health department, on the one hand, and by collateral agencies, on the other. Thus in the two extremes cited above, in Nevada about 22 per cent of total expenses for such work is spent through the state health department, while in Tennessee approximately 51 per cent is spent by the state health department. Again in Nevada special boards and commissions expend more than 50 per cent of the total, whereas in Tennessee special boards or commissions spend nothing (Table II). For the United States as a whole, state health departments expend 18.5 per cent of the total expended by state governments for all types of state health activities.

Table III gives information as to the sources of the $1.90 per capita that states spend for their various health activities. It should be noted that 81.4 per cent is state money, 3.9 per cent local,* 6.7 per cent federal, and 8 per cent from other sources.

The activities relating to health, carried on as functions of state agencies other than the state health department, are important, but in many instances they are on the periphery of the public health program rather than a part of its core, as conventionally recognized.

---

* The word "local" represents moneys received from local jurisdictions for services provided by state agencies. It does not include local appropriations for local health services.

Subsequent discussion, therefore, will be related essentially to state health departments, their organization and administration.

The Board of Health and the State Health Officer

As indicated previously, the nucleus around which state health work grew is the board of health. Members of this board, from five to seven in number, are usually appointed by the governor, though this is not always the case. From the state board of health was evolved the state health officer and around the state health officer was built up the state health department. As state governments became more organized and tended to establish themselves as cabinet systems, many boards of health were eliminated. In a few states this cabinet system evolved before the organization of a board of health and in these states there were no boards, as such. On the other hand, in spite of changes in other elements of state government, the state board of health has remained in some instances unchanged. The result is that in a few states ultimate authority continues to rest in the state board of health, in others the state board of health is vestigial, having only advisory functions, or has been replaced by an advisory council. Regardless of the evolution, there is at present a board of health or an advisory council or committee in all states of the Union except Idaho and Nebraska.

Boards of health in their old and true form were, and some still are, unique and powerful bodies. They represent one of the few instances where society has been willing to delegate to one group of individuals a combination of power in all three branches of government: executive, legislative, and judicial. These, by American tradition, are ordinarily kept quite separate. Technically, the board of health has executive power in that the health officer was, and in some instances still is, a subordinate and interim representative of the board. The board's power to promulgate regulations gives to it a quasi-legislative power in the field of public health, so long as its regulations are reasonable and remain within the intent of the laws upon which they are based. Semi-judicial functions are manifested by boards of health in their power to conduct hearings and render opinions which, while not having quite the status of the decisions of courts, are still powerful in their effect and in what they imply.

The individual who occupies the position of executive officer for the state board of health or who directs the work of the state health department is usually designated as the "state health officer." Actually, however, other terms are used officially. New York State has a commissioner of health, Arizona has a superintendent of health, Maine has a director of public health. In Louisiana the title is president of the state board of health; in Mississippi, executive officer of the state board of health; and in Kansas, secretary of the state board of health. The latter title indicates, for most state health officers, the ancestry of the position.

The state health officer is appointed by the governor in 26 states, and by the state board of health in 20. Idaho and Maine are the exceptions.* In some states the governor's nominations must be approved by the state board of health and in others the state board of health's designation must be approved by the governor. In a few instances, the governor's appointment must be confirmed by the state senate. Qualifications for state health officers vary. Generally, the appointee must be a physician. There is in most states a requirement that he shall have had some years of experience in the practice of medicine and a somewhat vague insistence that he shall "be skilled in sanitary science." Citizenship in the state concerned is a common requirement, and even where it is not is usually essential to appointment.

Salaries paid state health officers have a wide range, from $2,500 to $12,000 per annum, with a mean salary of a little over $5,000 a

* In Idaho a director of health is appointed by the Commissioner of Public Welfare, and in Maine by the Commissioner of Health and Welfare.

year. Appointments are for the governor's term of office or at his pleasure, though there are a few exceptions.

Organization and Functions of the State Health Department

There was set forth above a list of health and medical activities engaged in by state agencies of all sorts including the state health department. Inasmuch as it is the latter which is primarily concerned with conventional public health work, it is of interest to scrutinize those activities recommended by the American Public Health Association as desirable functions for a state health department (8). These are as follows:

1. Study of state health problems and planning for their solution as may be necessary.

2. Coordination and technical supervision of local health activities.

3. Financial aid to local health departments as required.

4. Enactment of regulations dealing with sanitation, disease control, and public health, which have the force of law throughout the state.

5. Establishment and enforcement of minimum standards of performance of work of health departments, particularly in communities receiving state aid for public health.

6. Maintenance of a central laboratory, and where necessary branch laboratories, for the standard functions of diagnostic, sanitary, and chemical examinations; production or procurement of therapeutic and prophylactic preparations, and their free distribution for public health purposes; establishment of standards for the conduct of diagnostic laboratories throughout the state; laboratory research into the causes and means of control of preventable diseases.

7. Collection, tabulation, and publication of vital statistics for each important political or health administrative unit of the state and for the state as a whole.

8. Collection and distribution of information concerning preventable diseases throughout the state.

9. Maintenance of safe quality of water supplies and control of the character of the disposal of human waste for all communities of the state.

10. Establishment and enforcement of minimum sanitary standards for milk supplies.

11. Provision for services to aid industry in the study and control of health hazards due to occupation.

12. Prescription of qualifications for certain public health personnel.

13. Formulation of plans in cooperation with other appropriate agencies for the prompt mobilization of services to meet the health needs.

For the performance of these functions, the state health agency is divided into various bureaus, divisions, and sections. In those states in which local health departments are relied upon as the principal mechanism for rendering direct public health service, the state health department is a comparatively small organization, a large proportion of its machinery being related to advisory and supervisory guidance of these local health departments. In states where the development of local health service does not constitute a major policy and principal objective of the state health department, the state organization is large, with centralized administration.

No attempt will be made, in this section, to describe the program of the state health department in terms of specific activities. Such activities may be put in proper perspective only if considered in relation to all levels of government: federal, state, local. Such a discussion will be found in Chapter V.

Expenditures by the State Health Department

Previous discussion of expenditures for state health work was related to the total amount expended by all state official agencies. This amount is approximately $285,715,800. Of this total the state

DEPARTMENT OF PUBLIC HEALTH, STATE OF TENNESSEE

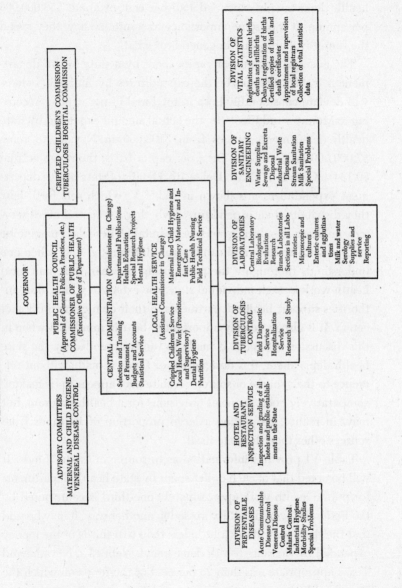

GOVERNOR

ADVISORY COMMITTEES
MATERNAL AND CHILD HYGIENE
VENEREAL DISEASE CONTROL

PUBLIC HEALTH COUNCIL
(Approval of General Policies, Practices, etc.)
COMMISSIONER OF PUBLIC HEALTH
(Executive Officer of Department)

CRIPPLED CHILDREN'S COMMISSION
TUBERCULOSIS HOSPITAL COMMISSION

CENTRAL ADMINISTRATION (Commissioner in Charge)
Selection and Training
  of Personnel
Budgets and Accounts
Statistical Service
Departmental Publications
Health Education
Special Research Projects
Mental Hygiene

LOCAL HEALTH SERVICE
(Assistant Commissioner in Charge)
Crippled Children's Service
Local Health Work (Promotional
  and Supervisory)
Dental Hygiene
Nutrition
Maternal and Child Hygiene and
  Emergency Maternity and In-
  fant Care
Public Health Nursing
Field Technical Service

DIVISION OF
PREVENTABLE
DISEASES
Acute Communicable
  Disease Control
Venereal Disease
  Control
Malaria Control
Industrial Hygiene
Morbidity Studies
Special Problems

HOTEL AND
RESTAURANT
INSPECTION SERVICE
Inspection and grading of all
hotels and public establish-
ments in the State

DIVISION OF
TUBERCULOSIS
CONTROL
Field Diagnostic
  Service
Hospitalization
  Service
Research and Study

DIVISION OF
LABORATORIES
Central Laboratory
Biologicals
Evaluation
Research
Branch Laboratories
Sections in all Labo-
  ratories:
Microscopic and
  cultures
Enteric cultures
  and agglutina-
  tions
Milk and water
Serology
Supplies and
  service
Reporting

DIVISION OF
SANITARY
ENGINEERING
Water Supplies
Sewage and Excreta
  Disposal
Industrial Waste
  Disposal
Stream Sanitation
Milk Sanitation
Special Problems

DIVISION OF VITAL STATISTICS
Registration of current births,
  deaths and stillbirths
Delayed registration of births
Certified copies of birth and
  death certificates
Appointment and supervision
  of local registrars
Collection of vital statistics
  data

health departments expended 18.5 per cent or about $53,000,000 per annum. It is of some importance to scrutinize how they spend the funds available, and in general for what.

The average amount per capita spent by a state health department is $0.395. Obviously, the expenditures by individual states will deviate considerably both in total and in per capita. According to Mountin and Flook (9), the actual amount expended by state health departments ranges from $103,000 in Nevada to some $7,000,000 in New York. On a per capita basis, the range is from $0.134 in Ohio to $1.682 in Delaware. Details of state health department expenditures are shown in Table V, which sets forth how they distribute their expenditures: whether for central office services, field services, local grants, or hospitals. These data need to be studied with caution and can be truly interpreted only when one understands thoroughly the relationship between state and local health work in each individual state, the extent to which local authorities support health departments in their own communities, et cetera. It is also extremely important to bear in mind that when in this discussion reference is made to funds expended by the state health department, this designation of funds is made without reference to their source or sources. A state may appear to be making comparatively good financial provisions for a health program, but may, in reality, be getting a large proportion of its funds from sources other than the state itself.

Table VI provides information as to source of "state" funds. It will be noted that of each dollar spent by state health departments for public health work approximately one-third is contributed by the Federal Government. Expressed in another way, it may be said that the state contributes a little less than two-thirds of the money expended by the state health department. Nebraska, Nevada, and Texas appropriate less than 25 per cent of the funds on which the state health department operates, and Delaware, Massachusetts,

TABLE V. Approximate total and per capita annual expenditures* by the health departments of each state and territory, the District of Columbia, and the Virgin Islands, and proportion of the total amount which was expended for each of several broad categories of service (9)

State or territory	Approximate annual health department expenditure*		Per cent of total expended for each service category			
	Total	Per capita	Central office services	Field services	Local grants	Hospitals
Total	$52,896,200	$0.395	23.3	35.2	21.3	20.2
Alabama	1,145,900	.404	21.4	32.0	46.6	
Arizona	176,700	.354	40.3	20.9	38.8	
Arkansas	642,400	.330	22.7	20.3	57.0	
California	2,451,400	.355	17.8	43.4	38.8	
Colorado	463,300	.412	38.9	44.1	17.0	
Connecticut	562,000	.329	38.2	56.7	5.1	
Delaware	448,300	1.682	25.3	25.5	5.1	44.1
District of Columbia	2,658,500	4.009	12.4	29.2		58.4
Florida	551,800	.291	38.1	41.8	20.1	
Georgia	1,145,700	.367	30.6	34.3	19.6	15.5
Idaho	253,400	.483	31.0	47.4	21.6	
Illinois	1,544,700	.196	18.8	72.0	9.2	
Indiana	664,900	.194	25.6	65.0	9.4	
Iowa	478,600	.189	33.1	58.8	8.1	
Kansas	405,000	.225	28.9	40.9	30.2	
Kentucky	1,010,500	.355	21.7	16.2	50.9	11.2
Louisiana	1,027,700	.435	17.9	53.4	28.7	
Maine	370,500	.438	21.9	78.1		
Maryland	763,500	.419	32.5	13.9	53.6	
Massachusetts	3,793,400	.879	7.3	41.0	13.8	37.9
Michigan	1,321,000	.251	51.4	18.2	30.4	
Minnesota	694,300	.249	21.8	74.4	3.8	
Mississippi	909,100	.416	22.7	17.5	39.2	20.6
Missouri	721,000	.191	24.5	61.3	14.2	
Montana	168,200	.301	27.0	41.7	31.3	
Nebraska	258,700	.197	54.4	45.6		
Nevada	102,900	.933	57.4	42.6		
New Hampshire	207,400	.422	36.0	57.6	6.4	
New Jersey	918,400	.221	26.0	67.9	6.1	
New Mexico	222,100	.418	43.0	18.5	38.5	
New York	6,990,400	.519	a33.6	a11.6	16.3	38.5
North Carolina	1,183,900	.331	21.9	34.1	44.0	
North Dakota	176,600	.275	33.9	47.3	18.8	
Ohio	926,000	.134	24.9	19.2	55.9	
Oklahoma	541,200	.232	32.0	34.9	33.1	
Oregon	284,100	.261	29.3	29.6	41.1	
Pennsylvania	3,693,200	.373	20.1	37.5		42.4
Rhode Island	792,600	1.111	12.9	30.7		56.4
South Carolina	886,000	.466	11.6	31.6	28.3	28.5
South Dakota	204,800	.319	21.3	43.2	35.5	
Tennessee	1,133,400	.389	28.7	40.1	31.2	
Texas	1,127,400	.178	26.5	36.4	37.1	
Utah	445,900	.810	12.9	68.0	1.6	
Vermont	181,600	.506	30.6	69.4		17.5
Virginia	1,872,900	.700	11.4	30.4	22.3	35.9
Washington	286,900	.165	38.5	24.5	37.0	
West Virginia	395,100	.208	43.5	22.7	33.8	
Wisconsin	643,400	.205	33.8	58.2	8.0	(b)
Wyoming	109,300	.436	16.7	83.3		
Alaska	171,200	2.344	22.8	70.1	7.1	
Hawaii	1,115,400	2.635	19.0	40.7	40.3	
Puerto Rico	3,507,200	1.876	12.5	28.6	24.0	34.9
Virgin Islands	146,000	5.866	10.4	20.1		69.5

* Because of variations in fiscal periods, figures cover the most recent year for which information was available at the date of interview.

a Because of New York's method of operation and reporting, it was not feasible to segregate all costs for the 19 state health districts from expenditures for general administration. Therefore, the proportion recorded for "central services" is inflated, while expenditures for "field services" appear to be much lower than is actually the case.

b Although operation of tuberculosis hospitals is now a function of the health department in Wisconsin, records for a complete fiscal year were not available under the new administrative set-up.

TABLE VI. Approximate total and per capita annual expenditures* by the health departments of each state and territory, the District of Columbia, and the Virgin Islands, and proportion of the total amount which was derived from each specified source (10)

| State or territory | Approximate annual health department expenditure* | | Per cent of total derived from each source | | | | | |
	Total	Per capita	State	Local	U. S. Public Health Service Title VI	U. S. Public Health Service V. D. funds	U. S. Children's Bureau Title V	Other
Total	$52,896,200	$0.395	63.1	1.6	17.1	5.3	10.4	2.5
Alabama	1,145,900	.404	42.1		25.7	12.4	12.7	7.1
Arizona	176,700	.354	25.7		31.6	7.8	33.8	1.1
Arkansas	642,400	.330	36.1		34.8	15.7	12.8	0.6
California	2,451,400	.355	62.7	4.9	12.8	6.9	10.5	2.2
Colorado	463,300	.412	31.4	6.1	26.9	7.0	28.6	
Connecticut	562,000	.329	65.4		17.7	4.4	12.5	
Delaware	448,300	1.682	78.3		9.5	1.2	11.0	
District of Col.	2,658,500	4.009	93.4		2.4	0.2	4.0	
Florida	551,800	.291	41.9		24.5	5.8	17.3	10.5
Georgia	1,145,700	.367	57.5	0.3	25.6	5.2	11.4	
Idaho	253,400	.483	38.5		28.6	5.8	27.1	
Illinois	1,544,700	.196	55.7		27.4	7.2	8.9	0.8
Indiana	664,900	.194	50.2	1.6	29.2	8.0	11.0	
Iowa	478,600	.189	33.9	5.5	37.7	8.4	10.3	4.2
Kansas	405,000	.225	32.9		33.6	13.0	17.6	2.9
Kentucky	1,010,500	.355	54.9		22.4	5.6	10.0	7.1
Louisiana	1,027,700	.435	70.2		16.6	3.4	9.8	
Maine	370,700	.438	34.1	5.2	17.5	2.3	24.6	16.3
Maryland	763,500	.419	57.5		17.1	3.2	22.2	
Massachusetts	3,793,400	.879	87.9		5.6	1.6	4.9	
Michigan	1,321,000	.251	47.0	1.2	20.8	8.6	8.4	14.0
Minnesota	694,300	.249	44.7	11.1	26.5	4.6	11.1	2.0
Mississippi	909,100	.416	51.4		23.4	10.4	11.2	3.6
Missouri	721,000	.191	32.0	5.0	37.6	10.7	14.5	0.2
Montana	168,200	.301	36.0		34.5	1.6	27.9	
Nebraska	258,700	.197	17.0	4.0	22.2	3.0	12.7	41.1
Nevada	102,900	.933	22.2	10.5	30.7	3.0	32.1	1.5
New Hampshire	207,400	.422	41.6		24.4	5.8	26.7	1.5
New Jersey	918,400	.221	58.5		24.4	7.3	9.8	
New Mexico	222,100	.418	27.7		32.2	3.9	36.2	
New York	6,990,400	.519	85.0		8.4	2.6	3.9	0.1
North Carolina	1,183,900	.331	36.0		26.4	4.4	19.4	13.8
North Dakota	176,600	.275	32.2	3.4	33.9	1.4	25.5	3.6
Ohio	926,200	.134	40.5		33.4	14.5	11.6	
Oklahoma	541,200	.232	34.2		34.5	16.3	7.8	7.2
Oregon	284,100	.261	27.9		32.3	10.4	23.9	5.5
Pennsylvania	3,693,200	.373	78.2		10.7	3.2	7.9	
Rhode Island	792,600	1.111	84.1		6.9	1.3	6.5	1.2
South Carolina	886,000	.466	50.9	2.5	22.0	5.8	17.9	0.9
South Dakota	204,800	.319	27.8		36.0	3.1	33.1	
Tennessee	1,133,400	.389	32.3	8.3	26.6	5.9	15.0	11.9
Texas	1,127,900	.178	22.8		37.0	23.1	16.0	1.1
Utah	445,900	.810	53.8	7.8	15.3	3.1	19.4	0.6
Vermont	181,600	.506	38.8	3.4	23.7	0.6	29.7	3.8
Virginia	1,872,900	.700	55.5	16.5	13.6	5.7	8.4	0.3
Washington	286,900	.165	35.0		37.1	14.4	12.3	1.2
West Virginia	395,100	.208	36.9		37.7	5.8	13.5	6.1
Wisconsin	643,400	.205	44.9		24.8	3.5	9.0	17.8
Wyoming	109,300	.436	36.5	0.3	25.2	1.5	36.5	
Alaska	171,200	2.344	17.3	14.3	23.7	1.2	40.7	2.8
Hawaii	1,115,400	2.635	84.4	1.0	5.2	1.2	5.6	2.6
Puerto Rico	3,507,200	1.876	81.7		7.5	3.4	7.4	
Virgin Islands	146,000	5.866	85.7		11.8	2.5		

* Because of variations in fiscal periods, figures cover the most recent year for which information was available at the date of interview.

New York, Pennsylvania, and Rhode Island contribute more than 75 per cent of state health department funds. Viewed from the standpoint of federal contributions, it is to be noted that the ratio of federal funds to total expenditure by states varies considerably as between the states. Funds from federal sources make up only 15 per cent of the total health department budget of New York State; only about 12 per cent of that of Massachusetts. But in many of the southern, middle western, and western states, federal aid accounts for more than 50 per cent of the amount that state health departments expend (10).

This divergence in the amount of aid which the Federal Government provides for the several states is not, as might be thought at first, due to political pressure or bungling. The allocation of federal funds to states is on the basis of weighting formulae which, if not perfect, are sound in their concepts, and in general tend to recognize economic conditions, needs, and resources in the several states. See pages 63 and 75 for methods of federal allotments.

From the standpoint of government and economics, two broad sociological problems are involved in this matter of federal grants-in-aid for health purposes. The first relates to the soundness of the general principle of federal grants. This was objected to strenuously by representatives of the American Medical Association in the White House Conference (see page 84) so far as concerned federal aid in public health; and the general idea is opposed by many as a government policy. Recent trends in American government, however, indicate that grants-in-aid of state and local public health work will remain as established procedures, unless there are changes and reversals in federal policies. The second sociological problem is the effect of federal grants in public health work upon the appropriating bodies and state health officers of the several states. Although it is quite difficult to prove, there has undoubtedly been a tendency on the part of some state legislatures, and on the part of state officers themselves, to look strongly and expectantly to the Federal Government, rather than to moneys collected as state taxes, for support and maintenance of public health services.

Certain General Considerations

As previously mentioned, the state is important in public health work because it is that sphere or stratum of government in which is vested authority for day-by-day health service to the citizen, whether this service is rendered by the state or by local health agencies. The state is also important because it is a transfer point or way station in the route of funds and influence arising in the Federal Government but destined for local health departments. Expressed otherwise, it can be said that the federal health agencies do not deal directly with local health departments, either in grants-in-aid or otherwise. They deal only with the state health department. The latter therefore occupies a strategic position, for state health officers as a group play some indirect part in determining federal health policies, and within certain limitations, each state health officer, in his own state, determines how and where and what health work is to be carried on.

This complexity of relationships makes it difficult to discuss the place of state health departments in the public health scheme without repeating what has already been said in connection with federal-state relationships, and what is to be said later in connection with state-local affairs. For these discussions reference is made to Chapters II and IV.

For many reasons, no one set pattern of public health activities would be suitable to all the forty-eight states. Their different laws and methods of procedure make this impossible from an administrative standpoint. Further, the extent and character of a state health program depend to no small degree upon elements which vary from one state to another: financial resources, race constitution, educational level, industrialization, and urbanization. Finally, in a country as large as the United States there are certain public health problems not common to all states, or more serious to one state than to another. But though there must be differences between the work of state health departments today and in the future, there are certain assets and liabilities that many or most of them have in common. Among the former it should be recognized that within the limitations imposed by their respective political and economic environments, state health departments are efficient, well-operated organizations; and state health officers are quite competent. Their deficiencies are in the direction of omissions.

One of the important limiting factors to many state health programs is that public health is not a live issue with governors and legislators. Because problems involved and solutions indicated are somewhat technical, such officials do not usually see the implications of a health situation as they would those bearing upon banking or public utilities. They are inclined, therefore, to leave well enough alone and to take action only when there is some dramatically dangerous situation or the pressure of public opinion. The state board of health, for its part, is quite powerful so far as concerns enforcement action for preventing the spread of communicable diseases, but is not conceded any great wisdom in statecraft that involves social and economic factors in health. There are exceptions, of course, but the above represents in general the situation that exists.

The state health officer himself, regardless of his professional competence and foresightedness, is also under a handicap as concerns extension and strengthening of his department's program. While he has the respect of most of those who make the laws, shape the policies, and provide the funds, he is of relatively low-grade rank in the hierarchy of state officials. His very nearness to the governor, as a member of the Cabinet, serves to handicap his freedom of action and liberty to introduce new proposals. After all, a state cabinet is a quite small group, and strained relations are inevitable if the state health officer does not hold the furthering of his health program within the bounds of the governor's interest, which is not necessarily great.

All these things have contributed to what in all fairness might be called an attitude of laissez-faire in many state health officers. Among some of them there is a tendency to subscribe to traditions, low budgets, and restricted programs. Worst of all, in those states where a substantial proportion of the population is without continuing efficient local health service, few state health officers appear to be acutely concerned with the situation; and most of them tend to acquiesce in the belief that local or localized health service for all communities of the state can be brought about only gradually and by opportunism and compromise.

If this view of the situation is anywhere nearly correct, it seems unlikely that a vigorous nation-wide program of public health service will be achieved merely by adding up the separate activities of forty-eight states. They must, on their several parts, play an important role in such a program, but to ensure health service to every community, wherever located, will require an extension and strengthening of federal-state-local undertakings to which reference has already been made and which will be discussed further.

REFERENCES

1. Act of the General Assembly of the Province of Carolina, June 7, 1712. An Act for the more effectual preventing the spreading of contagious distempers.
2. Whipple, George C. State Sanitation: A Review of the Work of the Massachusetts State Board of Health. Cambridge: Harvard University Press, 1917, vol. I, p. 30.
3. *Ibid.*, p. 291.
4. Mountin, Joseph W., and Flook, Evelyn. Distribution of Health Services in the Structure of State Government: The Composite Pattern of State Health Services. Public Health Reports, 56:1676, August 22, 1941.

5. *Ibid.*, Table 2, p. 1690.
6. *Ibid.*, Table 3, p. 1693.
7. *Ibid.*, Table 4, p. 1695.
8. American Public Health Association. Desirable Minimum Functions and Organization Principles for Health Activities. An Official Declaration of the American Public Health Association, adopted October 9, 1940. Year Book for 1940–41, p. 49.
9. Mountin, Joseph W., and Flook, Evelyn. Distribution of Health Services in the Structure of State Government: State Health Department Organization. Public Health Reports, 58:568, April 2, 1943.
10. *Ibid.*, Table 5, p. 572.

IV

LOCAL HEALTH DEPARTMENTS

IT is necessary ever to bear in mind that the vast majority of routine health service received by the people of the United States is delivered by local agencies. The Federal Government may subsidize and indirectly shape local health departments, the state health department may determine major policies for local agencies, set their standards, promulgate regulations, and even directly supervise them, but the final determining factor in the effectiveness of a public health program rests with the workers in the locality where the problems are occurring. In a few states, health workers in the smaller jurisdictions may be employees of the state health department, but more generally they are local employees: the greater part of their salaries is paid locally, and they function as a part of local government.

The extent and character of health service in a given township, county, or city developed, of necessity, within the framework of the constitution, public health laws, and regulations of the individual state in which that locality is situated. Growth or failure to grow was further influenced by social and economic factors of state and locality, by governmental policies and public attitude. The number of elements that have contributed to or retarded the development of local health service is, therefore, very great, too great to permit any place-by-place description or discussion.

In spite of this diversity of influences in the forty-eight states and thousands of localities, there were certain problems common to all, and a corresponding resemblance in measures undertaken for the solution of these problems. As a result there is today in the United States a fairly definitely established and uniform local public health practice; and though there is difference in detail, the rural health unit of an agricultural state, on the one hand, and the metropolitan health department, on the other, are basically similar. It is important, therefore, to pick up common threads in the development of local health service, for they may indicate why the present situation is as it is, and, more important, they may suggest future trends and needs.

It is important, too, to recognize how the population of the United States is distributed by size of community. This is indicated in Table VII. Expressed in another way, it may be said that there are, in Continental United States (exclusive of Alaska), 3,070 counties.

TABLE VII. Population in groups of places classified according to size, for the United States, 1940 (1)

Area and class of places	Number of places	Population	Per cent of total population
United States	–	131,669,275	100.0
Urban territory	3,464	74,423,702	56.5
Places of 1,000,000 or more	5	15,910,866	12.1
Places of 500,000 to 1,000,000	9	6,456,959	4.9
Places of 250,000 to 500,000	23	7,827,514	5.9
Places of 100,000 to 250,000	55	7,792,650	5.9
Places of 50,000 to 100,000	107	7,343,917	5.6
Places of 25,000 to 50,000	213	7,417,093	5.6
Places of 10,000 to 25,000	665	9,966,898	7.6
Places of 5,000 to 10,000	965	6,681,894	5.1
Places of 2,500 to 5,000	1,422	5,025,911	3.8
Rural territory	–	57,245,573	43.5
Incorporated places of 1,000 to 2,500	3,205	5,026,834	3.8
Incorporated places under 1,000	10,083	4,315,843	3.3
Unincorporated territory	–	47,902,896	36.4
Cumulative summary			
Places of 100,000 or more	92	37,987,989	28.9
Places of 25,000 or more	412	52,748,999	40.1
Places of 10,000 or more	1,077	62,715,897	47.6

Of these, 1,828 were served by local health units under the direction of a full-time health officer as of June 30, 1942 (2). The population of counties and municipalities served by such units constitutes about 75 per cent of the total population of the United States. The growth of governmental local health work, measured by the number of counties so served, was from 15 counties in 1915 to 726 counties in 1935; from 1,577 counties in 1940 to 1,828 counties as of June 30, 1942. In spite of this progress, there remained as of mid-year in 1942 some 33,000,000 persons in the United States without government-supported health service. The greater proportion of these people live in the smaller urban communities and in rural areas.

Origins of Local Health Services

Local health services began quite simply and modestly. There was the familiar sequence of pressing problem and attempted solution. Services did not arise as part of a careful plan for public health which would be state-wide or nation-wide and directed continuingly against potential as well as immediate problems. On the contrary, they originally came into existence under the urge of some specific emergency and tended to disappear as local memory of the trouble became less acute.

There were two principal situations that precipitated early action in the interest of the public health. The first of these was the epidemic, the second the necessity for providing some sort of medical care for those who through age, poverty, or misbehavior had become wards of the community. Epidemics brought brisk but temporary action in the nature of a board of health. The need for medical care was met by a fairly continuing but limited and somewhat grudgingly provided physician for the poorhouse and jail. In their beginnings, measures directed against epidemics and services for the care of medical wards were quite separate, and even in modern times local medical care is likely to constitute a part of welfare rather than health service. However, as local boards of health became more stabilized, with part-time health officers as their interim representatives, those officials were in many instances also made responsible for medical care of the community's wards.

This genesis of local health work reflects what generally happened, though there were a few significant exceptions. Recurring epidemics of yellow fever had in most communities led to a belief that the outbreaks were caused in some way by ships from foreign shores. This belief was shared by the majority of physicians, and measures designed to be preventive in nature were introduced at the various ports. An order of the General Court of Massachusetts, March 18, 1647 (or 1648), exemplifies early public health action of this sort (3). It provided that all ships coming to Boston from the West Indies must remain at anchor in the harbor and await permission of the Council before landing passengers or discharging cargo. The penalty for violation was £100. A reproduction of the order is shown on page 118. The order was repealed on May 2, 1649, "seeing it has pleased God to stay the sickness there" (West Indies). Responsibility for enforcing the provisions of this act rested with the Council itself, there being neither a medical officer nor a board of health at that time.

Jones (4) summarizes the administration of quarantine measures in the first century and a half of the town of Boston as follows:

> It appears that the early jurisdiction over quarantining was exercised by the Governor and Council of the Colony of Massachusetts Bay. Later it was carried on by the same, with the assistance of the selectmen of the town of Boston. These selectmen had the full power over quarantine conferred on them by an act passed in the year 1797. By the appointment of a Board of Health in 1799 all the powers of the selectmen over quarantine were delegated to this Board by an act passed June 20, 1799, and continued until the Board ceased to exist [1822].

For asmuch as this Co^{r}te is credibly informed y^t ye plague, or like greivos [in]fectious disease, hath lately exceed^{gly} raged in ye Barbadoes, Christophers, & oth^r i[slands] in ye West Indies, to ye great depopulat^g of those, it is therefore ord^{r}ed, y^t all [our own] or oth^r vessels come^g from any p̄ts of ye West Indies to Boston harbor shall stop [and come to an] anchor before they come at ye Castle, und^r ye pœnalty of 100£, & that no p̱son comeing in any vessell from the West Indies shall go a shore in any towne, village, or farme, or come within foure rods of any oth^r p̱son, but such as belongs to the vessels company y^t hee or shee came in, or any wayes land or convey any goods brought in any such vessels to any towne, villag^e, or farme aforesaid, or any oth^r place wthin this iurisdiction, except it be upon some iland where no inhabitant resides, wthout licence from ye councell, or some three of them, und^r ye aforesaid pœnalty of a hundred pound for ev^{r}y offence.

That no inhabitant, seaman, or other p̱son whatsoev^r, reciding wthin this iurisdiction, shall go a board any such shipp or vessell comeing from the West Indies aforesaid, or buy or otherwise take into his possession any goods or marchandize brought in any such vessell, wthout licence as aforesaid, und^r ye pœnalty of 100£, & to be otherwise confined or restrained, as the said councell, or some three of them, shall appoint; & to ye end y^t all p̱sons may have due information hereof, it is hereby agreed, y^t this ord^r shalbe forthwth published, & a coppy thereof sent to ye captaine of ye Castle, togeth^r wth com̄ission to him to cause ev^{r}y shipp or other vessell, belonging to ye country or any oth^r place, y^t shall come from any p̄t of the West Indies aforesaid, to stop & come to an anchor before they shall passe ye Castle, & then send unto them a coppy of this order, & there cause them to remaine till furth^r order from ye councell, or some three of them, whose counsell is to be taken therein; this ord^r to continue till this Co^{r}te or the councell of ye com̄on wealth shall see cause to repeale ye same.

It is furth^r ord^{r}ed, y^t a coppy of this order shall be forthwth sent to the sev^{r}all cunstables of ev^{r}y port towne in this iurisdiction, wth warrant to give notice thereof, wth all possible speed, to any vessell comeing from ye West Indies aforesaid, upon ye first veiw thereof, & furth^r to see to ye execution of this ord^r, according to ye utmost of their ability, & y^t ye councell, or some three of them, shall have pow^r to appoint some convenient place, upon some of ye ilands or oth^r fit places, where such p̱sons & goods shalbe sheltered for a time, & to do any thing of like nature y^t shall be necessary for their preservation, & welfare of ye country.

FIRST COURT ORDER REGULATING QUARANTINE OF VESSELS
Passed at a Session of the General Court, Colony of the Massachusetts Bay in New England, March, 1647 or 1648

A somewhat similar situation, differently handled, is to be f
in the action taken to prevent the introduction of disease
Charles Towne, in Carolina. Here, by an Act of the Provincial Legislature, October 8, 1698 (5), it is set forth that:

> All vessels are forbidden to pass to the east of Sullivan's
> Island one mile, without permission of the Governor, under pen-
> alty of being fired on by the gunner and paying a fine. The pilot
> is required to ascertain from the captain before passing that
> limit, if any contagious disorders are on board, under penalty of
> 50 pounds. [See also pages 201–208.]

From an administrative standpoint, perhaps the most significant
action of the late eighteenth century, bearing upon local public
health, was the Massachusetts Act of 1797 which made it possible,
though not automatic, for some of the more populous communities
to have boards of health. This legislation was further extended in
1849, with an increase in the number of local boards of health.
Similar provisions were being made in other states and undoubtedly a number of communities formed what were in effect boards
of health, or in one way or another provided some local mechanism
for dealing with health problems. But, so far as the record goes,
Petersburg, Virginia, in 1780, was the first locality to establish a
board of health (6). New York had one of some sort in 1796, Baltimore in 1798, the Town of Boston in 1799. As a rule, the establishment of these boards, as with all boards, indicated only that government was taking emergency action to meet an unusual situation;
and the fact that a board was formed at a given date does not mean,
necessarily, that it has continued ever since to operate. Quite frequently, as a local government became better organized, it substituted some other mechanism for the board of health. Thus the
Boston Board of Health was originally a township board. When
Boston organized local jurisdiction as a city, in 1822, no city board
of health was established but, instead, these functions were dis-

charged by the City Council, through committees. A city board of health, as such, was not established by Boston until 1872. Although of no particular significance, it is interesting to note that the President of the 1799 board was Paul Revere, who seems to have gotten around a good deal.

The public health work of local communities, especially of the smaller ones in the nineteenth century, may with fairness be described as desultory. A number of factors contributed to this. Public health was concerned only with the communicable diseases and, except in vaccination against smallpox, knowledge as to their control rested upon two procedures, quarantine and environmental sanitation. The latter was general rather than specific, aesthetic rather than scientific. There was a tendency to judge the danger of a situation in terms of unsightliness and smells, an inclination manifested even today.

As to the matter of quarantine, mentioned above as the first preoccupation in local health in the nineteenth century, it likewise was a generalized rather than a specific procedure. It was concerned more with imported than with indigenous diseases, as much with inanimate objects as with people, more with terminal than with concurrent disinfection. The local boards of health were unlikely to take any action except in the face of an epidemic; and the continuing high endemic and mortality levels of ordinary diseases, particularly those of childhood, did not as a rule cause any activity on the part of local authorities.

Aside from the lack of specific knowledge as to the causation, dissemination, and methods of control of the communicable diseases, there was another deterrent to the establishment of local health organizations and services: the people of the United States were keenly suspicious and distrustful of government executives of any sort. Most of the local grievances of the Colonies had arisen from what they regarded as arbitrary action on the part of administrators appointed to rule them, and they wanted a minimum of this sort of thing for the future. Further, so seldom did one then jostle elbows with his neighbors, that there seemed little need for a code of laws providing against remote contingencies of this sort. Administrative law, setting forth in a sort of preventive way the extent to which the citizen must curb his individual liberty of action in order not to jeopardize that of his fellow men, is comparatively a new thing, conceded grudgingly by the people. Until recently, therefore, public officials were at a minimum, and were limited to those necessary for the maintenance of law and order. An active health official was not regarded as being in this category.

There were, of course, and there still are, other deterrents to the development of local health service. In many instances the local jurisdictions concerned have been lacking in one or more of the elements necessary if a satisfactory health program is to be put into operation and maintained successfully. Some communities have not possessed sufficient wealth, some have been too small in population, some too large in area, some have been prohibited by law, or at least not enabled by law, to expend any funds or more than a pittance for public health purposes; some have suffered from ineffective or unwise state and local policies and tradition, or from the indifference of public opinion. Because these forces have continued to operate, and are still factors of importance, it would seem advisable to examine in more detail the common types of local health organizations that have grown up in this country.

Types of Local Health Organizations

Broadly speaking, official local public health work is divided into two categories: urban and rural. Small communities, classified technically as urban,* are more frequently rural than urban, but

* Bureau of the Census definition of "urban" is the one adopted in 1910 and slightly modified in 1920 and 1930 and includes cities and incorporated places of 2,500 or more population.

the characteristics of the city are fairly definite: population con-centration, established public health utilities (as water supplies, sewerage systems, garbage disposal), relative freedom from insects, centralized milk control; the resources of hospitals and clinics, con-centration of physicians, dentists, nurses; a higher educational level of population, community-wide transportation, well-organized public welfare, a concentration of wealth and assessable property; lay and professional support in public health matters; sometimes detrimental pressure of powerful political machines.

Most city health departments work quite independently of the state health departments, the city's charter, as a rule, providing a relatively high degree of local autonomy within the limitations of existing statutes. The work of one competent city health depart-ment is remarkably like that of another and, except in those fields where stability has been pretty well achieved in cities but not in rural areas, as in excreta disposal and water supplies, the program of the city health department is fundamentally the same as that operated by a county. Subsequent reference is made to these pro-grams, but for the moment attention is directed to the ways in which local rural public health work is carried on.

It has been previously indicated that community health organi-zations operated by government arise within local jurisdictions. This accounts for the fact that not all states have comparable local health organizations. New England, and that part of the interior and western part of the nation organized under the New England influence, utilize the town (township) as the local unit of govern-ment; those sections of the United States that adopted the system originally introduced on the southern Atlantic seaboard have es-tablished local government on a county basis.

Until full-time, well-rounded health organizations were recog-nized as the most satisfactory mechanism for ensuring effective lo-cal health service, it is likely that the township system, with a part-

time health officer for each small community, was the more productive. Other things being equal, this health officer had the advantage of a small jurisdiction, from no part of which could he be very
distant. In many instances, though, he was a lay person rather than
a physician, and this had its drawbacks. The county system of the
southern states provided a part-time physician for the entire
county. He served as health officer and not infrequently as jail and
poorhouse doctor. His great disadvantages were that he had a very
large territory and was paid from nothing to a couple of hundred
dollars a year. He could not, in the circumstances, do much more
than issue warnings about particularly objectionable hog pens and
privies in the county seat, occasionally tack up a quarantine plac-
ard, and vaccinate after smallpox appeared.

With a trend toward an organized health service, the average
county proved to be a more desirable administrative unit than did
the ordinary township. Generally it possessed greater wealth and a
population sufficient to make minimal health service economically
practicable. For these reasons, and perhaps others, active rural
health departments, as part of local government, have developed
more rapidly in the southern United States than in the north.

The county, however, is not in all ways the ideal unit for local
health administration. Many counties are deficient in the requisites
mentioned previously and, at best, the population and problems of
the average county are not great enough to utilize, completely,
specialized personnel and auxiliaries now considered essential, as
in tuberculosis, maternal and infant care, nutrition, et cetera. In
other instances, a county's financial resources may not be sufficient
to provide its budget quota for support of the well-rounded organization that is necessary even at a minimum. For these reasons, and
because the laws of some states restrict county expenditures for
health purposes, there has been a new trend toward the establishment of district health departments. These districts are of various

sorts and may forecast an advance in the development of local health service, or the reverse. Usually they are established by the state health department and, with or without the benefit of enabling legislation, form a part of state administration. In the absence of specific legislation, the arrangements made are quite informal and are not legally binding as concerns local authorities within the district.

In a consideration of the organization of health work on a district basis, it must be borne in mind that there are a number of different sorts of districts, and that the differences in their concepts and origins are significant. The principal types of district health departments are as follows:

1. *Combinations of local jurisdictions through mutual agreement of local authorities.* The local units combined may be townships or counties, but more often the latter than the former. In Massachusetts some years ago, for instance, two health districts were formed by combining townships* : Southern Berkshire with fifteen townships, and Nashoba, fourteen townships. Combinations of two or three counties to form a district health department are seen in most of the southern states. These districts have no status as units of civil government; they hang together because the contained local authorities have agreed to pool their resources for public health. The arrangement, ordinarily, is brought about through the stimulus and persuasion of the state health department, which agrees to subsidize the project. In most instances the procedure is an expedient, adopted because the local jurisdictions are too small or too poor to support separate services and, unfortunately, the budget and personnel provided are seldom adequate for the area or the population which they are designed to serve.

---

* In New England these civil jurisdictions are called "towns"; in most places the designation is "township." The latter term is here used to avoid confusion with that usage of "town" which means a small city.

Aside from the above handicaps, this type of district has within it certain inherent hazards. Being entirely voluntary, any contained jurisdiction can upset the whole arrangement by deciding that it no longer wishes to participate. Experience indicates that excuses for withdrawal are easy to find: one local jurisdiction thinks it is, proportionately, putting more money into the budget than is another, or that another is not putting in enough; a second is convinced that it is not getting its proportionate share of service; a third wants headquarters to be established in its area; and a fourth does not like the nurse or likes her too much. All these things have arisen to threaten or actually to destroy the district unit established on this basis. There is a final disability in this type of organization, in that the medical director, and his staff, must be appointed to official positions, severally and respectively, in as many local jurisdictions as the district contains. The director must deal with a corresponding number of local-authority groups in getting appropriations, and when local boards of health promulgate regulations he must remember that in one jurisdiction the isolation period for scarlet fever is three weeks but just across an imaginary line, or on the other side of a creek, isolation for the same disease is for a minimum of four weeks. However, in many instances no such disabilities arise and this sort of district remains continuingly in operation, helping to meet a situation that otherwise would not be met at all. As an expedient it is commendable but, even if it works satisfactorily, it is not a good permanent arrangement, for it was born in either financial or administrative poverty and its services cannot be comparable to what they should be.

2. *The state administrative and service district, created by regulation.* This sort of district, consisting of two to four or five counties, came into existence by state regulation rather than by law. It is designed to serve two principal purposes: 1) to provide localized administration of the program of the state health department and 2)

to render specialized or supplementary direct service to the people within the district. The function of this type of organization is not primarily to provide all basic health services needed in the contained local jurisdictions. For these, local authorities remain responsible, under supervision of the state district health department. If locally supported activities are deficient, say in public health nursing, the state staff may provide some service of this sort, or may in another instance arrange better tuberculosis or venereal-disease-control activities. The state pays for its personnel and its activities, the local jurisdictions for all or part of theirs. This is a far more modern and effective type of organization than that described previously, but inasmuch as the amount of funds provided by local health authorities is not uniform or related to any state-wide schedule, counties or other jurisdictions within the district do not always develop budgets adequate for needs. As with the mutual agreement combinations, there is danger that too little financial support by local authorities will finally be acquiesced in by the district health officer, and thus a low level of service may become accepted as satisfactory.

3. *The state administrative and service district created by law.* A few states have direct authority under the law to establish and maintain administrative and service districts designed to provide direct local health service. The exact arrangements vary. In one state all such service is paid for and directed by the state health department; in another the localities must participate financially and are required to become a part of the district; and in a third, while a district mechanism is provided for by law, participation is a matter of local option.

Administrative health districts for the provision of direct service offer great promise for the future, though at present those states which provide this mechanism suffer under one or both of two handicaps: 1) the funds made available by localities, or the state, or both, are meager; 2) the establishment of a district is dependent on the initial agreement of all the jurisdictions to be included in it.

Important in connection with local health administration is the fact that in 1942 the American Public Health Association appointed a committee to study the whole problem of ensuring local health service to all communities in the United States. This committee has proceeded, in general, with a plan that would provide legally authorized health districts as the mechanism for national coverage. In conference with the respective state health officers, it has visualized each state as divided into a suitable number of districts, none to contain less than 50,000 population. Standards for proportion of medical officers, nurses, sanitary engineers and other personnel, to population have been developed (7).

There will be some deterrents to the scheme and certain decisions must be made arbitrarily, as preliminaries. One of the difficulties is that the state health officer is likely to look with distrust at proposals coming from an outside group even if they are right; and inevitably, they will sometimes be wrong. Another and even more serious barrier to official health service on a district basis is that local and state politicians may be inclined to regard it as the first skirmish in a concerted attack on local autonomy and office-holding. In this connection, it is generally conceded that the most direct method of political suicide for a state legislator is to introduce a bill designed to do away with certain local offices. Sheriffs and auditors and clerks and superintendents and part-time health officers tend to rally to the support of the old order and the sacredness of local government. In the circumstances, many years, perhaps generations, will have to pass before all forty-eight states will be legally districted for purposes of better government and before present autonomous civil jurisdictions may be compelled to form a part of them. Perhaps, in the meantime, progress may be effected by a state-wide requirement that each local jurisdiction provide each year an amount proportionate to its resources, this amount to be supplemented by state (including federal) funds, and to be allocated to the maintenance of a health service organized along the lines set forth for a state health administrative and service district, as described above.

4. *The special sanitary district.* This type of district, as a rule, is created by special act of the legislature, in order to permit a particular community to institute some public health utility. Thus a suburban area might wish to build a sewerage system or provide a water supply or undertake malaria control. As an unincorporated area, it would not generally have authority to issue bonds or pass ordinances. Special legislation makes this possible. The sanitary district does not, in a true sense, provide a district health organization and is mentioned only to differentiate it from the other types described.

Basic Activities in Local Health Programs

Regardless of which civil administrative unit is utilized in providing local health service, it is generally agreed that certain activities are basic.

These essentials in the program are discussed at some length beginning on page 140, where the interrelations of federal, state, and local public health services are considered. For the moment, therefore, no program details will be presented, other than those provided in the summary of basic local health department activities, as laid down by the American Public Health Association (8). This summary is as follows:

Vital statistics: the collection, tabulation, analysis, interpretation and publication of reports of births, deaths, and notifiable diseases.

Sanitation: safeguarding all water supplies; securing the sanitary disposal of human and industrial wastes; supervision of the

HEALTH DEPARTMENT, BALTIMORE CITY

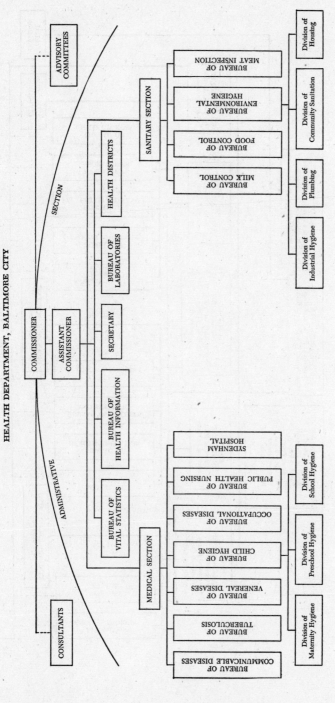

DEPARTMENT OF HEALTH, CITY OF NEW YORK

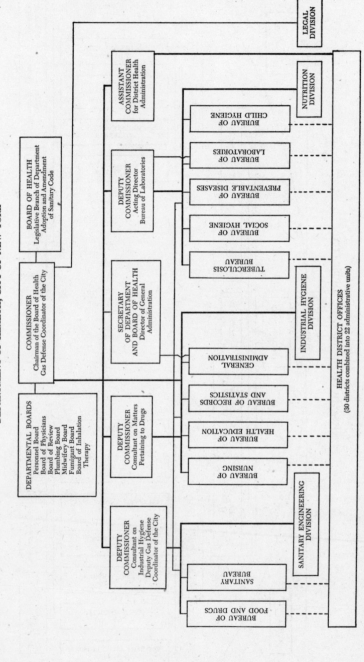

production and distribution of milk and milk products and of
foodstuffs; supervision of housing; control over the environmental sanitation of recreation areas and other public proper-
ties; control of insects and vermin as they affect the public
health; control over the environmental conditions of employment; and control over atmospheric pollution.

Control of communicable and preventable diseases: provision for the reporting of cases, the isolation of patients, and im-
munization of susceptible persons; systematic effort to find cases
of infection; and provision for diagnostic, consultative, and
treatment facilities where necessary.

Laboratory service: for the diagnosis of communicable diseases, for control of foods, and other features of general sanitation.

Protection of health in maternity, infancy, and childhood:
concern with the health status of the man and woman preparing
for marriage, of the expectant mother, of the newborn, the infant, the preschool and school child; and supervision of the conditions of work and the fitness to work of young people.

Public health education: to make health knowledge accessible
to the average man in a form that he can understand through
newspapers, magazines, books, pamphlets, lectures, personal
and group demonstrations, pictures and exhibitions, the film,
and the radio.

Costs of Local Health Service

It is not a simple matter to determine how much a given community is spending or should spend for public health work. One
may not establish a per capita expenditure by the simple expedient
of dividing the number of dollars in the health department budget
by the number in the population, for this budget sometimes contains items other than public health, or other departmental budgets may provide health items. Thus, one locality may include in its
figure on expenditures for health the cost for supervision of the
water supply. Another city may exclude these items from the

budget of the health department, charging them elsewhere. Again, in one locality but not in another, the local health department may carry on its budget the cost of school medical service. Other and similar differences in local budgeting for health might be enumerated, but these examples should suffice to indicate the variations and the difficulties of comparing the budget of one locality with that of another.

One might also raise a question as to whether or not per capita expenditure is a satisfactory index of health service, in view of the differences in health problems found in the thousands of localities in the United States, and in view of varying methods of allocating charges for ancillary services. Such a query cannot be answered categorically, but if in a given instance the quality and distribution of health service are what they should be, then it seems reasonable to express quantity in terms of cents or dollars per capita.

For a number of years it has been generally agreed that, to carry on a reasonably effective program, the annual budget of the local health department should be at least one dollar per capita, for con-

TABLE VIII. Per capita expenditures for health departments of eleven large cities, 1944 (9)

	Municipal funds	Federal, state, municipal, and voluntary agency funds
Boston	$1.18	$1.20
Buffalo	.93	.93
Cleveland	.76	.81
Detroit	1.01	1.02
Los Angeles	.55	.55
Milwaukee	1.00	1.00
New York	.88	.94
Philadelphia	.66	.67
Pittsburgh	.74	.74
St. Louis	.70	.81
Washington	1.27	1.57

ventional services. Table VIII indicates the per capita expenditures of eleven large cities in the United States, the amounts shown representing conventional health service operation, omitting the costs of water control, garbage collection, and other extraneous charges. These data are significant on two counts: first, expenditures reach a dollar per capita in only four of these cities, and in the remainder fall rather short of this goal; and second, the per capita expenditure from municipal funds is about the same as that from all sources combined. This is quite in contrast with the situation in health department budgets of smaller civil jurisdictions. Table IX

TABLE IX. Per capita appropriations for full-time county health organizations in operation *throughout any year* during the period 1908–33 (10)

Year	Number of states	Number of county organizations	Population of counties with health organizations a	Total budget		Budget of counties, county towns, and states	
				Amount	Per capita	Amount	Per capita
1908	1	1	36,757	$5,362	$0.15	$5,362	$0.15
1909	1	1	37,874	5,582	.15	5,582	.15
1910	1	1	38,992	13,480	.35	13,480	.35
1911	1	1	40,241	10,493	.26	10,493	.26
1912	3	3	151,851	33,203	.22	33,203	.22
1913	3	4	209,941	34,927	.17	34,927	.17
1914	3	b 7	283,400	55,859	.20	55,859	.20
1915	5	b 10	402,426	66,478	.17	66,478	.17
1916	6	c 14	916,919	84,750	.09	84,450	.09
1917	7	c 22	1,431,668	170,697	.12	161,045	.11
1918	11	d 36	1,925,115	330,205	.17	293,423	.15
1919	12	c 43	2,353,011	510,259	.22	460,778	.20
1920	16	e 81	3,744,053	889,694	.24	770,461	.21
1921	21	147	6,959,658	1,876,588	.27	1,655,024	.24
1922	24	176	8,161,266	2,139,657	.26	1,885,999	.23
1923	26	194	9,026,521	2,442,434	.27	2,104,598	.23
1924	30	b 243	11,017,267	3,284,466	.30	2,833,310	.26
1925	31	b 268	12,888,525	4,002,758	.31	3,484,048	.27
1926	33	c 310	15,719,742	4,673,393	.30	4,174,786	.27
1927	33	c 326	16,463,663	5,241,327	.32	4,775,727	.29
1928	35	d 413	19,473,585	6,572,641	.34	5,731,342	.29
1929	34	c 459	20,565,061	7,295,484	.35	6,463,653	.31
1930	35	c 504	22,318,002	8,059,061	.36	7,274,364	.33
1931	36	573	25,074,728	9,023,689	.36	7,576,491	.30
1932	34	559	25,067,651	8,114,436	.32	7,037,739	.28
1933	33	519	24,623,062	6,808,107	.28	6,091,816	.25

a Exclusive of cities of over 100,000 population in 1930, with the exception of Birmingham, Alabama, and San Diego, California, since these cities are served by their respective county health organizations. [Budget figures therefore differ slightly from those shown in Table X. They differ also because this table reflects appropriations for full-time county health organizations in operation throughout any year, whereas Table X includes also those in operation at any time in any year.]
b Data not available for 1 county.
c Data not available for 2 counties.
d Data not available for 3 counties.
e Data not available for 4 counties.

TABLE X. Number of full-time county health organizations in operation *at any time of the year;* total budget and source of funds for these organizations, 1908–33 (11)

Year	Number of county organizations	Total budget	Source of funds					
			Counties and county towns	States	U. S. Public Health Service	Rockefeller Foundation	Sheppard-Towner Fund	Other agencies
1908	1	$5,362	$5,362					
1909	1	5,582	5,582					
1910	1	13,480	13,480					
1911	3	21,180	21,180					
1912	4	35,286	35,286					
1913	a 7	49,177	49,177					
1914	a 8	58,859	58,859					
1915	b 14	76,311	76,311					
1916	b 17	91,350	90,250	$400		$700		
1917	b 30	194,437	164,512	12,413	$2,400	15,112		
1918	c 44	377,006	295,330	30,345	4,557	40,991		$5,783
1919	d 76	661,487	524,782	57,136	18,760	49,149		11,660
1920	e 138	1,215,141	907,243	153,911	20,141	93,151		40,695
1921	a 186	2,085,611	1,580,318	237,436	39,469	123,088		105,300
1922	211	2,318,251	1,741,874	265,064	51,460	134,537	$17,382	107,934
1923	237	2,716,901	1,996,066	339,149	44,732	152,968	29,424	154,562
1924	a 278	3,503,210	2,530,329	455,903	51,500	166,231	46,088	253,159
1925	b 316	4,245,850	3,129,571	548,420	70,939	153,053	71,243	272,624
1926	b 347	4,825,694	3,664,173	629,585	64,673	144,424	88,208	234,631
1927	b 426	5,592,223	4,263,777	748,591	120,605	185,674	66,730	206,846
1928	c 476	6,868,158	4,981,186	968,794	293,094	273,602	69,213	282,269
1929	b 519	7,529,429	5,518,649	1,116,685	325,259	265,961	40,407	262,468
1930	b 553	8,279,910	6,092,516	1,338,326	275,185	270,939		302,944
1931	610	9,208,402	6,153,708	1,516,482	986,977	144,828		406,407
1932	610	8,332,239	5,572,033	1,599,933	642,873	148,212		369,188
1933	569	7,135,361	4,954,447	1,414,075	118,631	150,277		497,931

a Data for 1 county not available.
b Data for 2 counties not available.
c Data for 3 counties not available.

d Data for 4 counties not available.
e Data for 5 counties not available.

shows, over a period of years through 1933, per capita appropriations for full-time county health organizations, and Table X indicates sources of funds. Noteworthy in these tables are the following:

1. Increase in the number of counties having local health service in a quarter of a century is gratifying but still leaves a lot to be done; see page 116 as to present status.
2. Even in full-time county and district health departments, service was quite thinly spread, as evidenced by the fact that $0.36 per capita is the maximum reached in any year.
3. Although local health departments up to and through 1933 obtained financial aid from a number of sources, funds other than those derived from state, county, and county

towns constituted only a small percentage of the total expended: a little more than 10 per cent in 1933.

4. In 1920, counties were subsidized by the respective states participating at the rate of about $1,100 each; this figure in 1930 was $2,400 per county, and in 1933 approximately $2,500.

Events in the financing of full-time county health service since 1933 are somewhat kaleidoscopic in character, in that shortly after that date emergency federal subsidies were made available, and in 1935 grants much larger than those previously received from federal sources were provided for state and local health service through Titles V and VI of the Social Security Act. Reference to this law and its provisions will be found in Chapter II, but here it may be said that these funds expanded and strengthened state and local public health work, particularly rural.

Looking back now, it would seem that the responsibility of local health authorities for provision of public health services has developed through a number of fairly definite stages. First, in early seacoast towns and frontier settlements, there was no formal provision for meeting public health problems. The situations that made themselves dramatically obvious, as epidemics, were handled as the need arose. Second, as provincial councils or state legislatures got to the matter, it was *permitted* that local jurisdictions might have a board of health. Third, as time passed, it was *required,* in a number of states, that each locality *must have* a board of health. Coincident with or following this, the requirement went further: each local jurisdiction *must have* a health officer, by custom part time. Fifth, through existing laws or new ones, local jurisdictions were *permitted* in most states to provide themselves with more nearly adequate health service: full-time personnel and a continuing program.

This brings the development nearly but not quite up to the present. It remains yet to be said that during the early part of the fifth phase state health departments took the role of salesmen. They bargained with and cajoled local authorities, all to the end that a local health department be established. They promised financial aid and sometimes got into trouble because Jurisdiction A drove a sharper bargain than Jurisdiction B, and the citizens of the latter became vocally and politically unhappy when they learned that A was getting more state aid than themselves. But by rule of thumb the state health departments fought their way on until they had gone about as far as they could in the circumstances. They had established health departments in most jurisdictions where some powerful political figure did not oppose them too vigorously; where the local medical society did not regard the proposal for a health department as a proposal for state medicine; where an entrenched specialized voluntary agency, sometimes subsidized by government funds, did not view the coming health department as a dark shadow; where the incumbent part-time local health officer did not mind yielding up his office.

When there was encountered the sort of difficulties referred to above, success was doubtful; and even where there was no opposition there were in most states a number of local jurisdictions that were unable to enter into the scheme because they were too small or too poor. Here the alternatives were intermittent specialized services from the state health department or a district organization of some sort.

As already mentioned, the amount, continuity, and balance of service rendered directly to local communities by the state health department or through district organizations vary from state to state. Often the service is inadequate to meet local needs, but even assuming that the three-fourths of the United States reached by localized health units actually receive ample health service, there remains the rather distressing fact that from thirty to thirty-five millions have not been provided with the benefits of the not inconsiderable public health knowledge at present available.

What might best be done in the circumstances will naturally vary from state to state. Further, such action as might be necessary to provide adequate local health service to every community in the nation involves more than local action, for with the limitations on taxation (in many places, only real estate is taxable by local government), *there are comparatively few local jurisdictions, outside the cities, that can alone support an adequate health program.* Further, if the local communities still without health service are to establish health departments or participate financially in a district health department, they need outside leadership and continuing advisory service. Because these matters involve state and federal health services, discussion of total action indicated will be presented in summary form as part of a final discussion.

But regardless of programs, funds, and guidance that may come to local health services from higher or larger governmental units, there are two things that are necessary if local communities are to participate in provision of health services for their own citizens.

1. The cycle of development of local health service (see page 135) must include another stage. Just as boards of health were first permitted and then required as part of local government, just as part-time local health officers first could be and later must be appointed, just as education was at first a limited privilege and later compulsory, so must adequate local health service go from the permissive to the mandatory stage.

This sentiment will be damned as impossible by many, and if efforts to bring it about are entered into in the several states in an apologetic, half-hearted way, it will not be carried through. Certainly, too, in some places, with no rewards or penalties involved, an undertaking of this sort would be stillborn.

2. The second necessity is to provide, through legislative enactment, suitable to the state in question, that local jurisdictions below certain populations and with a low ceiling on tax income shall for purposes of public health service form a part of a larger administration unit. This would apply to small counties, small towns, townships, and villages. In many instances, even when full-time health service is established for an area, some of its sub-units maintain themselves as little puddles of autonomy in the public health field, because the part-time health officer is the well-beloved community doctor.

In any event care would have to be exercised to avoid even the merest suggestion of general disturbance of local government. Any plan that proposed to abolish counties in the south or townships in New England would die of its own implications. Only the administration of public health service would be the issue involved. Parenthetically it might be said here that provision for mandatory financial support of local health service should not wait upon this requirement as to pooling of the health interests in local jurisdictions. With funds available, much could be done by informal local arrangements.

Throughout this discussion the term local health department has been used, and there has been an inference that local civil jurisdictions participate in providing and operating health services. This view reflects the general situation and is in keeping with the old concept of local responsibility for local benefits. It must be recognized, however, that a number of states, either because of legal provisions, as in Pennsylvania, or because of inability or unwillingness of local jurisdictions to provide funds, are rendering a considerable amount of direct local service through personnel employed entirely by the state health department. There remains, though, a thesis that people and local government ought to pay a part, at least, of the cost of benefits received. In the past this has seemed sound, but many now regard it as old-fashioned. If one is willing to waive this thesis, then there could be no objection to direct rendition of all local health service by the state, provided that: (a) it is adequate in amount and (b) it is a part of a continuing, coordinated, balanced, and effective program. Few services so rendered today would meet these requirements.

REFERENCES

1. United States Bureau of the Census. Sixteenth Census of the United States, 1940. Washington: 1942, vol. I, Number of Inhabitants, Table 9, p. 25.
2. Kratz, F. W. Status of Full-time Local Health Organization at the End of the Fiscal Year 1941–42. Public Health Reports, 58:345, February 26, 1943.
3. Records of the Governor and Company of the Massachusetts Bay in New England. Boston: William White, 1853, vol. II, p. 237.
4. Jones, Joseph. Surgical and Medical Memoirs. New Orleans: Printed for the author by L. Graham and Son, 1890, vol. III, pt. 1, p. 4.
5. Ibid., p. 2.
6. Toner, J. M. Boards of Health in the United States. Papers and Reports of the American Public Health Association. New York: The Association, 1873, vol. I, p. 502.
7. Emerson, Haven. Local Health Units for the Nation. New York: The Commonwealth Fund, 1945.
8. American Public Health Association. Desirable Minimum Functions and Organization Principles for Health Activities. An Official Declaration of the American Public Health Association, adopted October 9, 1940. Year Book for 1940–41, p. 46.
9. Municipal Year Book. Chicago: International City Managers Association, 1944, vol. XI, Table XIa, p. 368.
10. Ferrell, John A., and Mead, Pauline A. History of County Health Organizations in the United States, 1908–1933. Washington: Government Printing Office, 1936, p. 33 (Public Health Bulletin No. 222).
11. Ibid., p. 10.

V

ACTIVITIES OF GOVERNMENT IN A PUBLIC HEALTH PROGRAM

IT has often been said that both the strengths and the weaknesses of government in the United States depend upon the fact that there are three levels of government: federal, state, local. "Level" is probably not a good word to use here, for it implies graded powers, which is not altogether the case. Perhaps "areas of government" is a better term. In any event, the arrangement affects the conduct of public health programs to varying degrees, depending upon the item of public health service under consideration. Further, the public health program in one state differs from that in another, as do local programs in the same state. It is not possible, therefore, to make any blanket statement as to federal, state, and local interrelationships in all phases of public health, or to say that all local health departments have programs of exactly this or that content. There are, nevertheless, certain basic activities common to health department programs (see pages 103 and 128) and these are set forth below by disease concerned or activity prosecuted. In thus describing the current situation and practices, an attempt is made to indicate the degree and character of participation by each of the governments having an interest or responsibility. The description of any individual item, as tuberculosis or vital statistics, is necessarily sketchy, and should be considered against the general background laid down in preceding discussions.

Vital Statistics

Reports of births, stillbirths, and deaths are collected locally under the provisions of state laws. There are, therefore, forty-eight separate laws relating to the collection and preservation of vital statistics. Collections are made through a system of local registrars. The latter may or may not be a part of the local health organization. In cities there is usually one local registrar in the department of health, to whom all physicians and midwives report and to whom all undertakers apply for burial permits. In rural areas, because of distances, there may be eight or ten local registrars in each county, or one in each township, the town clerk perhaps. Original reports go from local registrars to the state registrars, directly or through the local health department. The state registrar may be the director of the Division of Vital Statistics or the state health officer himself. In only one state is the responsibility for collection and preservation of vital statistics in other than the state health department.

Local registrars are paid a fee of twenty-five to fifty cents for each certificate collected. Physicians and others making reports are not, as a rule, so paid. Certificates are checked locally for completeness, and so far as possible for correctness. Where there is adequate full-time local health service, the promptness, completeness, and accuracy of such reports are improved, as the health department's field personnel is rather well informed, particularly in rural areas, as to births and deaths. Many state and city health departments send to mothers of newborn infants a notice that the birth of their child is recorded. This is not, however, a certified copy of birth certificate. It gives name, sex, date of birth, et cetera, and if not entirely correct, parents tend to ask for correction.

In general, deaths are reported more completely and promptly than births, as the necessity for final disposition of a body impels physicians, undertakers, and registrars to sign the necessary documents. Fines may be imposed for failure to report births, stillbirths, and deaths, or for delay in reporting. Only in flagrant violations, however, is legal action taken. Reliance is placed more upon education and public attitude. The latter is a powerful influence. There is nothing in the civil requirements for registration of births

and deaths that in any way interferes with church registry of these
events should the citizen desire to do this also.

The Federal Government has no direct authority in connection
with the registration of births and deaths, yet it has a far-reaching
influence and has improved the situation markedly. It has proceeded along the following lines through the Division of Vital
Statistics, Bureau of the Census, Department of Commerce:

1. Participated in formulation of a Model Law for Vital Statistics, and encouraged the several states to adopt it.

2. Established a Federal Registration Area for Deaths in
1880, and one for births in 1915. Only those states with satisfactory laws, organization, and performance may have the credit
of belonging. All states have been in both areas since 1934.

3. Obtained acceptance by state and, therefore, by local
health departments, of standard forms and nomenclature.

4. Entered into arrangements whereby in each state an official
in the vital statistics system of the state is designated as a special
agent of the Census Bureau. That person is paid a small fee for
transcribing, or having transcribed, and sending to the Division
of Vital Statistics of the Census Bureau a copy of each certificate of birth, stillbirth, and death.

5. Provided that franked envelopes may be utilized in matters pertaining to the collection of vital statistics, such collection being regarded as of sufficient importance to the Federal
Government to justify this waiving of postage.

6. Publishes quite complete figures annually, under the title
Vital Statistics of the United States.

7. Exercises a mild and good-natured despotism, to the end
that standards be maintained in the collection and preservation
of vital statistics.

In recent years there has been a move to revise state vital statistics laws and forms in a way that would make them of greater
value as civil documents. The thought has been entertained, too,
that the Federal Government should enter more forcefully into the

situation, perhaps by establishing a collection system of its own. This has been given more consideration than heretofore because of increased migration from state to state, and in view of the inability of those born in states where birth registration is poor to prove, as a matter of record, parentage and place and date of birth.

The significance of the development of vital statistics programs as part of social and governmental evolution in the United States would appear to be about as follows. What was at first a church function has now become a governmental responsibility and is focused in the health department; in many localities, however, particularly in rural jurisdictions, the collection of vital statistics is quite separate from the public health program, though the general trend is to have it integrated with the activities of the local health department. In the Federal Government, these things stand out: (a) vital statistics activities are not a part of the principal health agency; (b) results are attained by leadership and persuasion, rather than through legal instruments; (c) increased movement of populations from state to state, and problems arising in connection with unemployment insurance, pensions, military registration, and other interstate affairs, make it entirely possible that in the not-too-distant future there will be legislation that would make the Federal Government far more active than now in the collection, preservation, analysis, and utilization of vital statistics.

Sanitation

This is what might be called an old-line activity of all health departments. The character of the program of sanitation varies in proportion to the size of the health department, its geographic location, its evolution. In most cities, the problems of excreta disposal, water supplies, and garbage removal have been rather completely solved or at least so stabilized that they may be classified as public health utilities, under maintenance management by departments of water supply or sanitation. The wise health officer, however, continues to keep a watch over the quality of the water supply and is informed and forehanded as to the possible creation of nuisances in the disposal of sewage and garbage. Inspection of foods, their processing, storage and preservation, and distribution are functions of the larger local health agencies. Both large and small are concerned with restaurant sanitation and with milk supplies. In some local and state health departments, especially in the south, insect control has an important place, and rat control is given attention in most seaport cities. The rural health departments have not stabilized their public health utilities, and so excreta disposal, water supplies, garbage removal in small towns, and the prevention and abatement of nuisances constitute a relatively large part of activities related to sanitation. State health departments support these activities through well-organized bureaus or divisions of sanitation.

Public water supplies are as a rule under the supervision of the state health department, or, if not, performance in water plants and quality of water must meet standards laid down by the state. Most states require that plans for water works or sewage disposal plants be submitted for approval. Pollution of streams by sewage or industrial wastes is also a state responsibility, rather than a local prerogative.

The Federal Government also enters into the sanitary program as it relates to water and stream pollution. Common carriers may serve to passengers only water that meets certain standards; navigable streams may not be polluted beyond certain limits. These functions are discharged by the United States Public Health Service, in the interest of interstate commerce, though army engineers have direct legal and indirect sanitary responsibility in navigable streams. Similarly, in the interstate shipment of meat, the Department of Agriculture exercises a rather complete and commendable inspectoral service.

Milk control programs are based upon ordinances passed by local authorities. The state health department encourages the passage of such ordinances but is not generally directly concerned with their administration. Not infrequently a state department of agriculture promulgates milk control regulations or works under a law that gives it authority to set standards as to market milk. These relate more to economics and food values, as percentage of cream and solids, than to sanitary quality of milk. The federal Department of Agriculture, too, has lent stimulus to improvement of the sanitary quality of milk through cooperation with the states in programs designed to eliminate tuberculosis, and more recently brucellosis, in cattle. To no small extent this department, through emphasis on high standards and procedures in handling milk, has encouraged many cities to adopt milk control ordinances. In recent years, public health education in sanitary control of milk and a standard milk ordinance have been fostered by the United States Public Health Service. There is not, however, any federal control as to the quality of milk shipped from one state to another.

The general trend in milk control is toward requirements for undiseased cattle, clean environment, trained and healthy personnel, cleanly and precise methods involving sterilization of containers, rapid cooling of milk and continuing refrigeration, all to the end that a clean product will result; and then, regardless of its assumed cleanliness and safety in this raw state, to pasteurize it. In most good milk control programs it is required that certified milk be pasteurized.

Insect control, as part of a sanitary program, may or may not be included in local health work. Previous to the reduction in the number of stables in cities, fly control received some attention. It is still a problem in small towns and rural areas. State health departments of the southern United States exercise leadership and provide some financial aid in mosquito control. The Federal Government, through an expert corps of sanitary engineers in the United States Public Health Service, has by demonstration and other means contributed to sanitary programs designed to eliminate breeding areas of *Anopheles* mosquitoes and, with experience now at hand, may soon be in a position to employ this method of malaria control on a scale more far-reaching than ever before. Problems in medical entomology, made more acute by World War II, have resulted in quite extensive research by the United States Bureau of Entomology and Plant Quarantine.

Other activities directed toward control of the environment, as in relation to housing, abatement of smoke nuisances, and even in connection with noise, have received attention, and perhaps as communal life and society grow more complex and social controls more far-reaching these and similar matters may more generally become responsibilities of health departments.

Acute Communicable Diseases

Perhaps the most interesting and significant aspects of this activity, one formerly participated in almost furiously by local, state, and federal health services, are that with the passage of time, old generalized control measures have given place to those designed specifically to reach a particular goal, and that, with the decrease in communicable diseases, activities for their control no longer constitute the essential reason for the health department's existence. The change in the problem itself may be grasped, in part, by examining the death rates from certain communicable diseases in 1900, 1920, and 1940. These are set forth in Table XI.

To present some of the reasons for these decreases would carry the discussion far afield. For present purposes it may be said that

TABLE XI. Number of deaths per 100,000 population, by selected causes, in the Death-Registration states of the United States as of 1900, 1920, and 1940 (1)

Cause of death	Number of deaths per 100,000 population		
	1940	1920	1900
Typhoid fever	1.0	7.6	31.3
Smallpox	0.0	0.6	0.3
Measles	0.5	8.8	13.3
Scarlet fever	0.5	4.6	9.6
Whooping cough	2.2	12.5	12.2
Diphtheria	1.1	15.3	40.3
Dysentery	1.9	4.0	12.0

in respect to many communicable diseases there exist sufficient knowledge and resources to hold them down to low endemic levels, but that where knowledge of transmission is meager, as in poliomyelitis or in those diseases that build rapidly to a vast number of uncontrollable foci and spread by close association, as the common cold, health authorities are in a position similar to that of boards of health of two centuries ago when faced with an epidemic of yellow fever: effective action must await an increase in knowledge.

From an administrative standpoint it may be recorded that the laws of all states require that communicable diseases be reported to the health authorities, usually the local health officer. Each state, by law or regulation, designates what diseases shall be considered communicable. Some also require reporting of diseases not communicable in nature, as occupational or nutritional diseases, and use the generic term "Reportable Diseases" to cover them all. The sequence of reporting a communicable disease is generally as follows: the physician, by telephone or mail (the requirements vary), advises the local health department or health officer that he has within his practice a case of the disease in question, and supplies identifying data; the health officer investigates or causes an investigation to be made, instituting what are currently considered to be control measures; the local health department periodically advises the state health department of the situation in its locality, furnishing copies of original records or summary tables that provide rather complete epidemiological data.

The Federal Government comes into this picture only indirectly. As a rule it is not administratively concerned with the endemic prevalence of disease, though it keeps careful check on this through weekly morbidity reports which each state health officer sends to the United States Public Health Service, and may take direct action if a local epidemic threatens to become interstate. The Service makes its greatest contributions through research in this field; through the grants-in-aid which it makes to states, and through them to local health departments, for improvement of health services; through its control over vaccines, sera, and similar materials that enter into interstate commerce; and through aid, counsel, and leadership. In the collection of morbidity data the Service occupies a position somewhat comparable to that of the federal Census Bureau in relation to the collection of vital statistics. The Public Health Service may appoint state and local health officers as collaborating epidemiologists and, with this federal status, they may use franked envelopes or post cards in making reports of communicable diseases. The Service also has authority over interstate movement of persons affected with certain communicable diseases. Previous reference has been made to the measures exercised to prevent the introduction of communicable diseases from abroad.

As part of their services for the control of the acute communicable diseases, most state health departments, through local organizations and designated distributing stations, supply physicians with vaccines and sera. The free availability of this material, beginning with smallpox vaccine and diphtheria antitoxin and now including a wide range of so-called biologicals, has played no small part in lowering incidence and death rates from those diseases which are preventable through the establishment of active immunity or curable through conferring an immediate passive resistance. In this free distribution of biologicals, however, there was, and perhaps still is, involved a question of principle: the wisdom of having government assume responsibility for supplying materials that one may, in ordinary circumstances, purchase in the open market. No one would question this procedure when the protection of the public is at stake or when a child might die because his parents have no money with which to buy diphtheria antitoxin. The matter has, though, gone much further than that and, in general, physicians in and outside of health departments tend to use free biologicals for cases that could quite well pay for them. On the whole, the abundant availability of material of this sort is so highly important and the results achieved are so good as to constitute, in the opinion of most people, ample justification for the policy of no questions asked as to indigence. In a discussion of this sort, however, the matter may not be passed over without notice as it is of considerable significance as a social policy.

Closely related to the above discussion is the question how far the health department should go in the actual administration of vaccines of one sort or another. Many physicians feel that, as a public function, this health department activity should be limited to medically indigent individuals, leaving to the care of the private physicians those able to pay. They find, for instance, that a southern rural health department, in a current year, administered typhoid vaccine to 3,000 individuals. Assuming that at least half of these could have paid for the service, physicians estimate a loss of revenue of some $4,500 because of health department competition. The matter, however, is not so simple as that, and though a generation ago few would have argued against the physician's contention that this service on the part of the health department should go to none able to pay, there are now practical considerations and a public attitude that must temper judgment on this question.

From the health department standpoint, the situation appears to be about as follows: the community level of many diseases can be reduced only if a considerable proportion of the population is transformed from susceptibles to immunes; it is the health department's responsibility to ensure such a transformation through one mechanism or another; only by mass action can relative population immunity be achieved and, in achieving it, it is as important to include the rich as the poor; it cannot be achieved by private physicians alone, for with smallpox vaccination available for nearly a century and a half, the people of most communities, in the absence of a health department, but with private practitioners available, remain unvaccinated.

The health officer further contends that the practicing physician is wrong in the assumption that as the number of persons vaccinated through the health department increases, the number using the services of the private physician for the purpose is reduced. The fact is that the number of persons willing to be vaccinated against one disease or another is vastly increased through the public health education and exhortation of the health department, a type of publicity that private physicians are not organized for and may not indulge in as individuals. So that although the physicians in private practice might not have been called upon to vaccinate 1,500 well-to-do persons against typhoid fever in the instance cited above, they would have given more vaccine in that year than previously, as a result of awakened public interest. Finally, as a last and practical point, the public health administrator emphasizes that in vaccination programs, carried on as a rule through clinics which large numbers attend, it would be impossible even if desirable to insist that each person, in a line of a hundred, establish medical indigence. Reaching the mass is the objective, and middle class and rich are part of the mass, and taxpayers.

The above discussion is presented at some length, because it is typical of those situations where there must be a choice between respect for the restriction of government activity in favor of free enterprise, on the one hand, and, on the other, violation of an established concept in order to meet current needs. The trend appears to be in the latter direction.

Tuberculosis

There is extreme variation in the amount and character of anti-tuberculosis work carried out in the various localities of the United States, and in the several states. To a greater or less extent, the local health department employs or participates in three types of control measures: 1) health education, 2) case finding, 3) disposition (for treatment and breaking of contract) of cases found. Each of these has by-products.

As is the case generally, the results of health education in tuberculosis are not exactly measurable. But that these results are cumulative and effective is shown by a comparison of public knowledge of, and interest in, the disease as of today and fifty years ago. Practically every health department makes some contribution, direct and indirect, through health education.

Case finding is complex, and is only now beginning to shape itself as a fairly clear and effective procedure. Only a short time ago the search for cases was limited to taking the history and making physical examination of those known to have been exposed to tuberculosis: contacts. Too often, attention was focused on the children, school children in particular, of the family concerned. This is an unfortunate selection for two reasons: first, because physical examination did not reveal the presence of the so-called "childhood type" of tuberculosis (primary phase), and second, of all groups in which the re-infection phase occurs, children of elementary school age are least affected. Some health departments, for want of better facilities, still must place reliance on physical examinations; and many health departments, even though they have x-ray facilities available, continue to sift school children, rather than adults, in an effort to find new cases.

Larger health departments ordinarily conduct regular tuberculosis clinics, provide consultation service for physicians, have nurses investigate families in which cases arise, aid in getting hospital care, attempt through welfare agencies to solve economic problems of patients and their families. The more forward-looking local health departments, within the limitations of their resources, now search for tuberculosis, quite independently of known contact, by mass x-ray surveys: an aggressive campaign, hunting cases rather than awaiting them.

Where the local health department is deficient in resources or the population is too small to justify assembly of complete equipment, facilities, and staff, most state health departments assist through itinerant clinics or through district organization. The problem of care of cases and separation of foci from others will be taken up subsequently.

It is obvious that a logical and effective attack upon tuberculosis must be based upon the known characteristics of the disease, upon knowledge as to prevention and therapy and, in terms of community resources, facilities and public attitude. But the subject is so vast that no attempt can here be made to analyze and assign weight to all those factors that enter into its epidemiology and control. As a background for discussion, however, certain outstanding points may be considered briefly.

The death rate from tuberculosis of the respiratory system in the United States, in 1942, was 39.6 per 100,000 population. In 1900 it was 175. In the past and at present, death rates in the several states and individual cities vary widely from the death rate of the nation as a whole. Thus the West North Central group of states have the lowest tuberculosis death rate, 25 in 1942, with Nebraska down to 12.6. The highest rate, 53, was in the East South Central states, with Tennessee at 64. This was not, however, the highest rate from pulmonary tuberculosis in 1942. The highest rate, 122.7, was in Arizona, a sanatorium state, with many Mexicans.

In spite of geographic variations in tuberculosis death rates, other factors than mere location enter into the situation. One must take cognizance of the influence of immediate environment, race, sex, age, occupation, economic status, educational level, et cetera. These contributing influences are so inextricably interwoven, one with another, that it is difficult if not impossible to recognize and measure their comparative importance in determining tuberculosis morbidity and mortality. Because of this there is danger that one might focus attention upon one factor to the exclusion of others, upon race to the exclusion of occupation, upon housing to the exclusion of educational level.

Obviously, great progress has been made in control of tuberculosis; equally obviously, much remains to be done. It may be said with fairness that no locality or state or the Federal Government has ever conducted an even reasonably adequate program for the control of the disease. A part of this deficiency arises because tuberculosis, as much as any disease and more than most, is a disease whose roots of origin and dissemination go deep down into the social, economic, and educational strata of the community, and whose control demands governmental and social action quite beyond the limits of the practicing physician and even beyond the scope of the public health program. Thus good wages and a fairly decent educational level constitute a necessary foundation for public health control of tuberculosis. They cannot be brought about overnight, or distributed as one would distribute pamphlets. But not all the deficiencies in the anti-tuberculosis program exist because of in-ability to establish a social order that would eliminate want. There is, as of today, and there has been for a long time, a great deal more applicable knowledge than has been used. Legislative bodies have never faced the problem of tuberculosis control squarely or com-pletely as they would a business or commercial situation. The re-sult is that comparatively few health departments have sufficient funds to carry out what should be routine activities, as case finding and hospitalization.

Those communities in which, with only a short wait, cases of tuberculosis may obtain sanatorium treatment are not typical of the United States as a whole. Twelve states in 1940 had not yet reached the original goal of as many hospital beds for tuberculosis as there are deaths from that disease annually. Actually, for the United States in 1940, there were only 1.46 beds per annual death, and this does not indicate that these beds were equally distributed over the country as a whole or entirely free or that, even among those designated as free, one could obtain their use without declar-ing oneself, officially and embarrassingly, an object of charity. Within the problem of hospitalization, too, is a practice that must be modified if the full effect of mass control is to become operative. This relates to the type of case admitted and discharged. To some extent there is a conflict of thought here. From the standpoint of the individual, admission in the minimal stage of the disease is highly desirable; and a high ratio of minimal to total cases admitted suggests early discovery of tuberculosis and, to that extent, good public health handling of the situation. On the other hand is the hard fact that it is the sputum-positive case that constitutes the immediate menace to others, and there ought to be no barrier to the admission of advanced cases. Those who view the matter from the public health standpoint are inclined to give admission priority to sputum-positive cases, regardless of stage, in order to break an established or immediately potential chain of transmission. Sanatorium directors, approaching the problem in terms of likelihood of obtaining recoveries, are sometimes loath to have far-advanced cases occupy beds badly needed for those who have a better chance of survival. Neither of these groups of cases needs to be served to the exclusion of the other if even reasonably adequate hospital facilities are made available.

Freer use of the x-ray and its increased adaptability to rapid examination of large groups have emphasized many facts previously suspected. One of these is the relative frequency of subclinical cases of tuberculosis: cases that present no symptoms and, on conventional physical examination, no signs that might lead one to suspect the presence of the disease. Mass x-ray surveys are therefore becoming an established method of approach for early discovery of tuberculosis. Here it would seem well to bear in mind that diagnosis is only fact-finding. The facts themselves are sterile unless something is done about them. It would seem somewhat footless, except for better delineation of the problem, to conduct mass surveys and discover, among other things, cases with minimal tuberculosis, in a community whose sanatorium facilities are inadequate to meet the needs of cases already known to exist.

The above represent some of the problems that have a bearing on the tuberculosis program for which local, state, and federal health services are or might be responsible. Matters such as better housing, living wages, proper nutrition, a higher level of education, fall outside the fields of medicine and public health administration, but there seems no reason why health authorities and the medical profession should not lend their support to a solution of them. It is no longer good public health work, if ever it was, to regard a case of tuberculosis as merely an instance where the life cycles of two species, the tubercle bacillus and man, have impinged one on the other. Clarity of viewpoint and competence in action demand that control programs extend to an eradication or minimization of all factors, social and economic, that enter into the situation.

Within the past year a new force has entered into the tuberculosis situation. This manifests itself in recent Congressional action which suggests that the Federal Government may engage, continuingly and aggressively, in a program designed to push the incidence of that disease to an irreducible minimum. The Act (2) provides for a federal appropriation of $10,000,000 per annum, to be used in education and research and in subsidy of state and local tuberculosis work. It is but a beginning, and will permit attack on only selected phases of the problem, but even this is encouraging.

It seems not amiss to mention in connection with tuberculosis that this is a field into which most official health agencies had to be led, if not drawn. It was approached reluctantly and apprehensively and even now is handled somewhat timorously. The public was so long used to having people catch consumption and die with it that early health workers tended to acquiesce in this lethargy of attitude. The disease lacks the drama of the epidemic; it is not a loathsome condition, there is little pain, no startling rash or violent mental symptoms, and those who go down before it die gently and on the whole inoffensively, so far as the community is concerned. New action and continuing action, therefore, did not come so much from those in the health department, for they could get no money from the duly elected authorities and perhaps on their own part lacked imagination. Instead, leadership came more largely from the people themselves. The focal point of this interest and the source from which most stimulation arose was the National Tuberculosis Association, with its state and local constituent organizations and its professional and lay membership. Leadership such as this represents the best in voluntary citizen-participation in public health work, a model that might well be followed in gaining public support of other phases of public health activities.

Venereal Diseases

All three areas of government, local, state, and national, participate in programs designed to control the spread of venereal diseases. In addition, strong voluntary agencies, particularly the American Social Hygiene Association, make valuable contributions in this field. In general, venereal disease programs have been concerned with only syphilis and gonorrhea, and until comparatively recently efforts were directed mainly toward syphilis control.

Two significant factors have strongly influenced the conduct of venereal disease control programs in local health departments. The first of these is that because there is no measure practicable for ensuring avoidance of contact, and no vaccine that might artificially transform susceptibles into immunes, syphilis and gonorrhea must be attacked along lines designed to eliminate individual foci. This carried health department programs rather sharply into the field of curative medicine, even though the goal in view was the protection of the public rather than benefit to the infected person. The second significant element is that, although health departments have attempted in their control program to view syphilis and gonorrhea as they would any communicable disease, the moral and social factors concerned have had to be considered to some extent.

Practically all local health departments operate clinics for the control of venereal disease and, as complementary to these clinics, conduct epidemiological investigations wherein an attempt is made to discover the source contacts, and possible spread contacts in each case. The state health department participates indirectly and ordinarily along the following lines: it establishes standards; it provides laboratory service for aid in diagnosis; it may provide for free distribution of drugs; it has available a consultation service for local health departments; and it conducts a continuing program of public health education. The Federal Government, likewise, operates along indirect lines of public health education, research, publication of a monthly bulletin, *Venereal Disease Information,* makes available to states the consultation services of competent experts, and finally distributes currently among the states, in aid of their venereal disease programs, some $11,000,000. Federal activities are through the United States Public Health Service and the amount currently available is higher than usual, having been increased to meet situations arising out of war activities in industry.

The direction and the extensiveness and intensity of the venereal disease program in the future cannot at this moment be forecast, but certain broad trends may be picked up if the past is viewed in perspective. Contrary to what is generally thought, public and professional interest in, and hopes for, control of venereal diseases is not a recent thing. Samuel D. Gross, at a meeting of the American Medical Association, called attention to the need for action in 1874, but the committee appointed appears to have given most of its thought to the problem of prostitution, and very little came of this effort. However, J. Marion Sims, who was President of the American Medical Association in 1876, in his presidential address was vigorous in his recommendations as to measures for the control of syphilis. Among other things he had the following to say:

> Medicine has done much for the relief of individual suffering, and for the prolongation of human life; but now, giving aid to governments and municipalities, it is instituting organizations for the prevention and suppression of disease on a scale of efficiency and grandeur never known before.
>
> State Medicine does everything necessary to protect the

health of communities and States. It investigates the air we breathe, the water we drink, the food we eat, the clothes we wear, the fuel we burn, the house we live in, the soil we cultivate, the habits and industries of life, the origin and nature of endemics and epidemics, the method of their transmission, and the means of their prevention and of their suppression wherever found.

Its object is to discover the causes, and to prevent the origination of disease, to prevent its spread, to circumvent it, to extinguish it, whether it be zymotic, contagious, or specific. In short, it is the function of State Medicine to protect the public health, which is the life of the nation.

While our Sections of Medicine, Surgery, and Obstetrics deal with subjects touching the welfare of the individual, that of State Medicine and Public Hygiene deals with subjects touching the welfare of the masses.

If yellow fever threatens to invade our precincts, we take steps to arrest its progress at once. If cholera sounds the alarm, we immediately prepare to defend ourselves against its ravages. If smallpox infests our borders, we circumvent and extinguish it. But a greater scourge than yellow fever and cholera and smallpox combined is quietly installed in our midst, sapping the foundations of society, poisoning the sources of life, rendering existence miserable, and deteriorating the whole human family.

Now what I propose in regard to syphilis, is simply to give to the already existing boards of health, in the various cities, the same power over syphilis that they now possess over cholera, smallpox, and yellow fever. They now have the power of ferreting out smallpox, and of sending it to hospitals for treatment; and they should have the same power of searching out the abode of syphilis, and of sending its victims to hospitals for treatment (3).

Dr. Sims' recommendations, as was the case with Dr. Gross, were not followed up and the medical profession and the public apparently decided to let well enough alone for more than a generation.

The second wave of interest arose incident to the first World War. As a result of steps taken at that time, there was established in the United States Public Health Service in 1918 (4) a Division of Venereal Diseases; and out of this interest, too, most of the states passed venereal disease control laws. These laws were based upon a model made available by the Public Health Service, and while they vary slightly from state to state, the basic requirements and provisions are quite similar. In brief they require, or provide, that physicians shall report venereal diseases to the local health officer having jurisdiction, in one state by name, in another by serial number; that modified isolation, designed to prevent spread, be imposed upon cases in the active stage of these diseases; that should the individual violate the restrictions imposed, he or she may be effectively segregated; that where cases desert treatment, the private physician must report the fact and provide the name and address of the individual to the health department; that clinics for indigent or medically indigent be supplied by local authorities; that there be supplied, also, free laboratory work and free drugs where necessary.

Previous to the adoption of venereal disease laws, all states had provided by law or regulation for instillation of silver nitrate or comparable solution in the eyes of newborn infants and, coincident with or subsequent to the adoption of venereal disease laws, many states, 33 by 1945, enacted legislation requiring that physicians include Wassermann or other serological examination as part of the care of prenatal cases. Thirty-one states now (1945) require serological examination pending issue of marriage licenses.

The federal interest in venereal disease control, born of World War I, died down as that war and its problems receded into the past. Federal provision for financial grants in support of venereal disease programs in the states was completely eliminated in 1928, and the activities of the Public Health Service in this field reached a low ebb and remained at this level until the passage of the Social Security Act in 1935. Under this Act the Public Health Service was able to use, for state aid in venereal disease control, some of the general-purpose funds provided. In the meantime, however, an active and far-reaching educational campaign in relation to venereal disease was having its effect on public thinking. Radio programs and newspapers, to which previously the words syphilis and gonorrhea were taboo, lifted these prohibitions, and better public understanding and a higher degree of interest were developed. Finally in 1938 the Venereal Disease Control Act (5) was passed and this tended to stabilize and to promise more permanency of federal participation.

Whether or not this participation will continue, only the future will tell. Like the enthusiasm of 1918, the present wave of interest arose to some extent out of war psychology or preparation for war, when it is easier to obtain an appropriation of a million dollars than it is ordinarily to get one of a thousand. Encouraging, however, is the fact that whereas previous interest in venereal diseases was limited to a relatively small group of experts, the present interest has a much broader base and a rather remarkable public support.

Apropos of control of syphilis and gonorrhea, it should be mentioned that newer therapy, as penicillin in early syphilis and sulfa drugs and penicillin in gonorrhea, may rather markedly modify the present public health programs in this connection. When administration of arsenic and bismuth was the only available treatment of early syphilis, and when irrigation was the main reliance in the treatment of gonorrhea, the control programs were necessarily built around venereal disease clinics. Newer therapy, if early promises come to fruition, will not require special skill or equipment, and the treatment of cases by penicillin could be carried out in the physician's office. While such widespread and active participation by private physicians in the treatment of these venereal diseases has much to commend it, there might be a loss in another direction: prompt and careful search for source and spread contacts could not be carried out by the practitioner as is done by the investigator working from the venereal disease clinic. If the clinic is not to continue as a strong element in the program, arrangements must be made for proper epidemiological investigation under some other auspices.

Laboratory Services

The character of service rendered in the public health laboratory differs from that provided in a laboratory of clinical pathology. The former is limited to examinations of materials that arise from cases or situations that have a public health significance. Thus, water and milk examinations are routine, as are specimens or cultures in relation to communicable diseases: diphtheria, tuberculosis, typhoid fever, gonorrhea, syphilis, rabies, et cetera. However, analyses and procedures that might contribute to the diagnosis of non-communicable diseases are not at present considered a function of public health laboratories except in special programs or incident to research. Urine examinations are made in connection with a maternal hygiene program, but not as an aid in the diagnosis of nephritis. From one standpoint this is quite consistent. Viewed in another way, it is not at all so.

The organization for laboratory service in health departments is comparatively simple: the large health departments maintain their own local laboratories, the smaller ones depend upon laboratories operated by the state health department. The latter agencies vary only slightly in the manner of supplying this type of service. The more populous and wealthy states have a district system, so that no local health department is far, in terms of mail hours, from one of these laboratories. In other states there is only a central laboratory.

The rather widespread provision of laboratory examinations as a public health service undoubtedly represented, in its inception, an initiation into a changing order: a service to the individual citizen, whether indigent or not. Theoretically, of course, it was a service designed to protect the public as a whole, but practically it represented government competing with private laboratories. Perhaps the sharpest clash of this sort arose incident to increased activities in relation to syphilis. Offering free Wassermann and other serological examinations to the citizens through private physicians and clinics rather completely put the private serological laboratory out of business. Regrettable as this might be, and even if it is alarming sociologically, there seems no doubt that free serological examinations constitute an essential part of a syphilis control program, and this laboratory activity is now generally accepted by private physicians and medical associations.

The Federal Government renders but little direct public health laboratory service. The United States Public Health Service engages extensively in research into the laboratory aspects of communicable diseases, particularly those in which the life history of the causative agent is not fully established. In instances where research necessitates obtaining large numbers of specimens for study purposes, the Public Health Service welcomes material and will report upon it. Again, where in relation to a particular disease, as psittacosis or lymphocytic choriomeningitis, that Service has accumulated knowledge, expertness, and facilities not immediately available from state laboratories, specimens have been received and reports made. Essentially, however, the National Institute of Health, which is the laboratory of the United States Public Health Service, is designed for and operates as a research institute.

A certain amount of laboratory work is also carried out by other federal agencies, but more often as incident to its major administrative function than as a direct service to the citizen. The Federal Trade Commission must have laboratory work in the prevention of commercial fraud, and some of this has a bearing on the public health. The Pure Food and Drug Administration of the Federal Security Agency similarly must have laboratory substantiation of evidence in prosecutions for violation of food and drug acts; and the Department of Agriculture, in its research in nutrition, in diseases of animals that might also affect man, and in relation to insects, must operate laboratory services that overlap to some extent the public health field. The Federal Government, however, maintains no diagnostic laboratory service comparable in purpose to those maintained by state and city health departments.

Nutrition

The problems of nutrition are being attacked by a number of special groups. There is some disagreement as to the exact status of knowledge in this field, as to the applicability of that knowledge, and as to how a service designed to improve the nutritional condition of the public might best be organized. Among those who may be said to be active in "nutrition" are the following: physicians, particularly pediatricians; laboratory workers engaged in research, some of whom, in the past, have not been greatly interested in the application of their findings; foundations, which are approaching the matter broadly and conservatively; those who are designated as home economists and nutritionists, with a scientific past not always clearly defined but possessed of great zeal and potentialities; and finally, those who have something to sell, usually vitamins and minerals in a special combination, under registered proprietary title.

Knowledge of this subject in relation to the public health has only recently shaken off empiricism and catch phrases, and is now to some extent assayable in scientific terms. Information formerly more or less academic in character is commencing to find its way into practice; methods and techniques are becoming more sharply defined and exact, and preventive and therapeutic measures more specific. The old term "malnutrition," once considered a quite exact clinical designation, is now recognized as being no more specific than is the diagnosis of "fever," and as all inclusive as was "eczema" in its older usage.

With this newer knowledge has come also a realization that just as there are subclinical cases of communicable diseases, so are there instances of subclinical manifestations of nutritional deficiencies that fall far short of presenting classic examples, say, of pellagra or beriberi. And perhaps the parallelism holds, also, in the ratio between clinical and subclinical manifestations. It has been suspected that in some communities, even in certain sections of the nation, a high proportion of the population suffers from one or more nutritional deficiencies. Undoubtedly this is the case in a few instances, but such general statements arise more often from over-enthusiasm than on the basis of evidence at hand.

The factors responsible for nutritional inadequacies in some parts of the public are, obviously, quite complex. Custom in the choice of food and in its cooking, its availability, the matter of funds with which to purchase it, are influences that focus around the individual and the family. As more remote but still definite influences are agriculture, transportation, and processing in relation to grains, fruits, vegetables, meats, milk and milk products, and other food substances. These things, to a greater or less extent, have a bearing upon the kinds and amount of foods in a nation's dietary, upon what goes into it, and what is taken out between raw state and the kitchen of the consumer. Many of the problems related to this aspect of the matter must be approached on a national rather than on a state or local basis.

Here is a situation, then, where a considerable medical knowledge has quite recently accumulated. It has become evident that there is a vast field where these new facts might be applied. Methods of applying this knowledge must now be worked out but, because the problem is so great and has such ramifications, it is not an easy one to solve. It is not one where, as in ensuring a safe public water supply, all the water drunk by the community can be channeled through a filter and there be chlorinated by a small group of professionals, with the individual citizen assuming no responsibility other than payment of the professionals' salaries. Nor may it be approached by doing something for each citizen only once or twice in his lifetime, as by vaccination in the control of smallpox. Once vaccinated, the individual can forget the matter for the time being and go about his business with a protection that lasts fairly long. But one cannot forget nutritional needs until the eating of a balanced ration becomes a habit; and even after it is a habit, the food one buys from the grocer or baker must not have been robbed of ingredients that it is supposed to contain.

A program of nutrition then must be broadly conceived and buttressed by national and state laws as to manufacture and processing of foods and food products, by freedom from economic distress, by agricultural development, by marketing arrangements, by community education. In other words it must be a function of federal, state, and local agencies in the field of public health and in allied activities that bear upon food.

Few local health departments yet conduct intensive nutrition programs, though a considerable amount of such work is done incident to maternal and child hygiene, dental hygiene, public health nursing, and by similar channels through which the public may be taught in matters of health. There are two weaknesses in this incidental approach. The first is that, at best, nutrition will remain to some extent a secondary consideration and will not be recognized as of major importance in its own right; the second is that the extent and degree to which the nutrition program reaches the public must remain limited to those groups reached by the major activities to which it is attached. In this instance, the limitation is essentially to children and, while it is important to reach children, it is not enough.

As regards nutrition programs in local health departments, however, it must be recognized that there is danger that enthusiasm and hope may run beyond knowledge and administrative machinery. This is particularly a menace in view of radio and press publicity as to the virtue and necessity of vitamins in pill form. Perhaps before local health departments venture too far in what is not yet an entirely charted field, state health organizations should build this activity into their organizations.

Hygiene of Maternity and Young Childhood

Practically all local health departments provide services in these fields of public health. Supporting them in these activities, through consultation and advisory services and with grants-in-aid, are the respective state health departments. In turn, behind the state programs in maternal and child health are federal grants made available through Title V of the Social Security Act, administered by the Children's Bureau. State and local health departments twenty years ago found working with the Children's Bureau somewhat trying, as it was difficult to incorporate into a generalized health service the limited-duty personnel paid for by these funds. As time has passed, greater administrative facility has been achieved, though even now the situation remains somewhat artificial and awkward.

It would seem unwise to attempt to describe in detail the operation of the conventional maternal and infant hygiene program. Perhaps it is sufficient to say in relation to the former that the objective is to provide, directly or indirectly, effective antepartum observation, safe environment and circumstances at delivery, and decent after-care. In the hygiene of infants and young children, the goals are essentially the same as in preventive pediatrics. Clinics, conferences, and home visits enter into both maternal and child health services and both are built around good medical supervision, rendered by the physician in either a private or a clinic capacity.

Measures of effectiveness in these fields are not easy to obtain unless one considers the health department program the sole factor responsible for the lowering of the maternal death rate and the infant mortality rate. Certainly it must have contributed to the improved situation, directly through specialized services and indirectly through safer water and milk supplies and through health education. But other factors, outside the health department, are extremely important: improvement in pediatrics, increased knowledge of nutrition, better housing, improved economic conditions, better educated young women, a fashion for the mother to take the infant regularly for medical advice—all these have played their part in lowering the death rate among infants and young children.

Deaths from puerperal causes have also been decreased by factors largely independent of the local health department's program for maternal care. Here, again, an expanding medical knowledge has been a determining factor, as have the increased availability and utilization of hospitals for delivery of normal as well as abnormal obstetrical cases. The public, too, has more and more come to accept the fact that good obstetrical care includes observation in the antepartum period. Perhaps the latter state of mind has been contributed to by the public health programs as much as by any other influence.

With these qualifications and cautions in mind, and regardless of the exact part played by each operating force, it may be said that the maternal and infant mortality rates for the United States have decreased markedly and on the whole in a satisfactory manner. Without going into details as to causes of death and age at death, and with no separations as to race, sex, or locality, the trend in infant mortality may be summarized as follows. In 1915, there were 100 deaths of infants under one year of age per 1,000 live births in the part of the United States at that time included in the United States Registration Area for Births (6). The states in that area, only ten in number and the District of Columbia, were all in the northern tier, and since the northern states have always had lower infant mortality rates than the southern, the true national rate would certainly have been higher than 100 had data for the whole country been available. In 1920, the infant mortality rate was 86. In the ensuing decade many states in the South, with high rates, particularly among Negroes, were admitted to the Registration Area for Births. This did not, however, halt the downward trend, and by 1930 the infant mortality rate had dropped to 65. In 1940 it was 47, and in the last year for which data are available, 1942, the infant mortality rate for all states and the District of Columbia was 40.4 deaths under one year of age per 1,000 live births.

Rates in maternal mortality also reflect a downward trend though not so fast or steady as that exhibited in infant mortality. Data as to deaths from these causes have been accumulated on a national basis only as the Birth Registration Area has grown, and the same considerations mentioned as to changing constitution of the Area in relation to infant mortality apply in connection with maternal mortality. The number of deaths from puerperal causes, per 1,000 live births (the maternal mortality rate) in the Birth Registration Area of the United States, as constituted in 1915, was 6.1. In 1920 it was 8. Only once in the past thirty years was that rate exceeded, when a figure of 9.2 was reached in 1918. In both 1918 and 1920 influenza was a factor. In 1930 the situation was worse than in 1915: the rate was 6.7. Not only had the rate remained rather static in those states that were in the Birth Registration Area in 1915, but there had been added to the Area many states with rates of more than 10. In the decade following 1930 there was a fairly rapid decline, so that by 1940, for the nation, the maternal mortality was 3.8 deaths from puerperal causes per 1,000 live births. In 1942, it was 2.6.

While, as mentioned in other instances, a detailed analysis of infant and maternal mortality is not here apropos, an element in each demands emphasis in any plans for extension or intensification of public health work in these fields. In regard to the former, it must be noted that the decline in the infant mortality rate has come about mainly through a saving of lives of babies three months of age and older. Although there has been a reduction in deaths in the first three months of life, it is not so great as in older infants, and the death rate in the first day of life has decreased only slightly since 1915. As to maternal mortality, attention may be called to a conclusion reached by the New York Academy of Medicine in a study of deaths from puerperal causes in that city in 1930–32 (7). This was to the effect that maternal mortality, then a little over 6 in the United States, and a little under 6 in New York City, could be reduced at least two-thirds; that deaths from the most common causes, abortion, hemorrhage, septicemia, and toxemia, could probably have been prevented in about three-fourths of instances in which they occurred. That goal has not yet been reached. Its attainment, therefore, remains for further consideration in programs designed to conserve maternal and infant health.

School Hygiene

This is a public health activity in which there is considerable confusion and where, to too great an extent, tradition rules. For these reasons it is a situation that demands attention. The way school health work is carried on in the United States varies greatly from state to state, and as between localities in the same state. In one place it is a function of the health department; in another, of the educational authorities. In certain circumstances, the program is desultory; in others it is promoted almost passionately. Nowhere is it quite what it should be. Its principal defect is that it produces little, and the main reason for this seems to be that the instruction received in health education is theoretical rather than applied and that, from a medical standpoint, the program focuses on getting children examined rather than on obtaining corrections of defects found at the examination. Local health officers have long been cognizant of this situation, particularly as to the failure to obtain correction of defects found. Perhaps they have been too ready to accept the fact that community facilities are not sufficient to meet the needs. In extenuation, however, it must be recognized that health departments lack funds to establish these facilities themselves, and both private physicians and hospital authorities have frowned upon such ventures by health officers when funds in rare instances were available.

In this situation, the medical procedures of school health work, except in relation to communicable diseases, grind on year after year, as a rule finding and re-finding the same defect in the same child. It is of interest, and important here, to point out that any physician experienced in examining school children could quite accurately have forecast the distribution of physical defects found by Selective Service in the examination of young men for the Army and Navy. The public was greatly astonished to learn of this deplorable condition in manpower. But that same public had been told, and retold, by notices from the school physician ten to fifteen years before, and often by visits of a nurse, that these future selectees had bad teeth, diseased tonsils, defective vision, poor hearing, orthopedic disturbances.

Except in those places where the department of education not only provides health instruction, but also employs its own physicians and nurses, all local health departments participate in school health work. This is usually limited to the elementary grades, and consists of a somewhat cursory physical examination designed to discover the more common remediable defects in the shortest possible time. Parents are notified of findings, and there are hopes that the child may be taken to the family physician or clinic for further examination and action. To this end the nurse as a rule visits the home. But full productivity in this phase of school health work may not be looked for until the child who needs his teeth filled or must have glasses put on him has a place to go and get it done. That is the first and primary need. A second is to narrow the gap between public health and education at state capitals, to the end that there be better coordination of effort in the field. Studies along these lines are now in process.

In the Federal Government, school health work has grown up as an accessory of education rather than of health. Theoretically, the principal agency concerned is the Office of Education, once a part of the Department of the Interior, now in the Federal Security Agency. Its program has very little influence upon front-line work as carried out by local health departments, as its contacts are with state departments of education, not health. The United States Children's Bureau exerts an indirect influence through its subsidy of state health programs. Similarly, the United States Public Health Service, though having no specialized activity relating to school health work, financially aids states and, through them, local health services which, in their general activities, reach children of school age. It may be said that here is a field where there is overlapping of federal functions.

In connection with this subject, and because the federal agency directly commissioned for school hygiene is also responsible in the physical education field, it seems wise to call attention to past and present agitation for national non-military physical education programs. Such moves have behind them the rather populous and not meanly organized school teacher groups. Further, especially in view of Selective Service findings, most laymen will support any move which they are told will ensure a more healthy youth. It seems inevitable, therefore, that sooner or later a bill for a nation-wide physical education program will get through Congress. No one will deprecate the desirability of robust exercise at this period of youth, though there is no scientific proof that the lad with a bulging chest expansion or the muscularly strong and tough football player will live any longer or be less subject to colds and syphilis than will his unathletic fellow student. But there is a real danger that uninformed enthusiasm may lead Congress, as in the past it has led parents, to believe that prevention of disease is rather completely assured by a physical education program; that an hour a day in the gymnasium or on the playfield, or two weeks in the mountains or at the seashore, will produce an immunity to diphtheria or smallpox or meningitis, or will prevent or correct caries, or offset an advancing myopia. Medical organizations, it would seem, might render a real service by making these points clear when legislation is proposed. It would be a very good thing psychologically, from the standpoint of morale, and perhaps even physically, for the nation to have a physical education program but, in the decisions, Congress should be informed of the limitations of such an undertaking. Provisions for physical education cannot take the place of public health service under medical direction.

Other Activities and Problems

In addition to the elements of health department programs already discussed, there are others to which attention should be directed but which the limitation of space makes it impossible to present in any detail.

Some of these draw together many basic elements of the program and concentrate them on a special group, as industrial hygiene; others cut across or contribute to a wide variety of basic activities, as public health nursing, health education, statistical services. Still others relate to fields of tremendous importance, but in which knowledge, techniques, and funds are lacking, as heart disease, cancer, mental disabilities.

Considering these subjects somewhat in the order mentioned, the following brief comments may be made.

Industrial hygiene. Forces that have contributed to the present great interest in this subject are: 1) the increasing national importance of industry; 2) the organization and increased strength of labor; 3) the war program, which has catapulted new and untrained millions into industry; 4) the introduction of new materials and processes into industry; 5) a crystallizing recognition of the fact that certain occupations and industries entail unusual and peculiar hazards to health.

Doubtless the present great interest in industrial hygiene will recede to some extent at the close of the present war, but in spite of this, industrial hygiene must be given serious consideration as an essential element of national, state, and local health programs.

Federal administration of industrial hygiene programs is complicated and divided among a number of different departments of government, but is now tending to focus in the United States Public Health Service.

Many states, particularly the industrial states, conduct industrial hygiene programs. The administrative agency is usually the state health department though, as in New York State, this activity might be more closely associated with an agency primarily concerned with labor.

The amount and character of industrial hygiene carried on by city health departments, seldom by rural health units, reflect to some extent the degree of industrialization of the community.

Perhaps the most significant and potentially effective element in industrial hygiene is that medical care is recognized as an integral part of the program. In the industrial population various prepayment medical insurance schemes have been developed and much has been learned through trial and error.

It is possible that this experience may establish a base for a more far-reaching public medical service; it is possible, too, that out of the group reached by industrial hygiene programs may come a pressure toward an extension of medical care under governmental auspices.

Health education. It is difficult to describe exactly the character and extent of programs in this field. The term itself refers to the measures that health agencies exercise in an effort to bring about in individuals, or in society, the regular and intelligent doing of things believed to maintain health and prevent disease, and the abstinence from those things considered injurious to health.

Health education is an undertaking that produces its results slowly, and these results are difficult to measure. It is especially necessary in those phases of public health where protection of the individual can be achieved only by that person's own effort; and, in relation to the community as a whole, it is essential in gaining public support of a health program. All health departments, local, state, and federal, engage in health education. In some fields, fairly effective programs are in continuous operation; in others, efforts are sporadic.

What is taught in health education and how it is presented to the public are two quite different things. What is taught ought to be true; not infrequently it is only a half truth, or an assumption; or something is urged which, while desirable in general, is not necessarily related to health.

How this material is presented to the public involves approaches and procedures quite foreign to medicine: publicity, dramatization, community organization, et cetera.

Commercial health agencies and many voluntary and professional agencies are more effective in health education than are health departments. Thus insurance companies, once convinced of the soundness of the investment, employ the best obtainable talent in advertising, commercial art, and printing. Their results reflect this.

A new "profession," known as "health educators," is arising. Too often these workers are without the restraint that comes from scientific training and are not well grounded in factual material relating to health and disease. They do, however, possess a stimulating enthusiasm and, in varying degrees, competence in catching the public interest.

The schools and colleges, particularly teachers colleges, offer excellent channels for certain features of the health education program. Much could be accomplished if the teachers in elementary schools had some sound knowledge of public health.

Public health nursing. No operating health agency could conduct a satisfactory program without the public health nurse or her counterpart. In the conventional health department program, from 40 to 60 per cent of the total local budget is allocated to this service. The community goal for public health nurses, in normal times, was one nurse to each 2,000 population.

Activities within this field contribute to practically every element of the health department program. Nurses are not, however, always utilized to the best advantage. Part of this appears to be due to health officers' ineptness in the use of a keen tool, some of it to an extreme guild consciousness on the part of nurses.

Any plans for extension of public health work, for intensification along already established lines, or for new undertakings must include serious consideration of the place of public health nursing. Possibly future developments may make it desirable to modify and improve the character and type of instruction and training of those who are to go into this field.

Dental problems in public health. Dental caries is the most frequent defect encountered in persons under middle age, and pyorrhea looms large as a disability in and after the fourth decade of life. In comparison with the size of this problem, dental programs rendered by federal, state, and local governments are quite inadequate.

Federal health agencies participate directly or indirectly in dental services along one or more of three lines: 1) direct service to certain groups, as dental care of beneficiaries of the United States Public Health Service; 2) indirect service, through grants-in-aid to states; 3) research in dental aspects of public health, mainly by the United States Public Health Service.

The dental programs of state health departments naturally vary, as do those carried on in cities and smaller civil jurisdictions. Such programs concern children mainly, and are conducted along two lines: reparative work and health education. The deficiency in the first is that it is only reparative: the correction of disturbances that have already occurred. A program of this sort could be carried on indefinitely without in any way decreasing the number of new cases that occur. The dental health education program is handicapped by the meagerness of knowledge as to how to prevent caries or pyorrhea. Information given must therefore be general rather than specific, complex rather than simple, and of a nature that demands an almost meticulous day-by-day performance from cradle to grave, which is more than most people can bear.

Cost has always acted as a deterrent to the development of programs for better dental health. No one can know just what a well-rounded program, including care, public education, and research, would cost, for experience is lacking. It seems likely, however, that such an undertaking, even if the immediate benefits were limited to children, would demand a larger budget than that now provided for all other health services. In the circumstances, it would seem sensible to include among the next steps to be taken an intensification of research and an exploration of administrative machinery and costs.

Mental hygiene. Few health departments, as such, conduct programs in mental hygiene. The principal care offered by government is institutional, as a rule operated by some agency other than that concerned with the public health. Such care is generally limited to those with disturbed mental states. Aside from the economic losses to the individuals and families concerned, and quite without regard to suffering and distress, the cost of caring for those affected is prodigious. It would be good business to relieve society of this cost, if possible.

Obviously, the difficulties in developing an effective mental hygiene program are vast. Viewed as would be a problem of control of a communicable disease, knowledge of prevention is scant; subclinical cases far outnumber clinical ones. These subclinical cases not only fail to develop a resistance, as a person would after a mild attack of typhoid fever, but remain as a reservoir from which drain typical cases; and typical cases are subject to relapse. Measures to assure a protected environment would involve far more than the control of inanimate material and non-human species, as in the case of malaria; the individual would have to be protected against all the stresses and strains occasioned by daily living and human relationships—relationships with the wife or husband, children, the boss, the butcher, the public utility. And two other things stand out: the difficulty of discovering who is a potential misfit or psychopath, and the fact that even if all adjustments could be made, the problem of many an individual might rest upon the quality of genes released by forebears some generations ago and only now focusing in him.

These difficulties need not, however, produce a defeatist attitude and do not justify such an attitude. Although the problem demands continuing and intensive research, there already exists considerable knowledge as to the psychology of children which makes it possible to avoid the development of fears and phobias and ingrown personalities. One obvious means of approach is through the educational system, another through adult education, particularly of parents. School teachers and even college professors might function as parts of a long-range plan; and pediatricians and public health nurses have immediate and day-by-day opportunities. Better coordination of effort between psychiatric institutions and public health activities is indicated. For the moment, however, it would seem that the incorporation of mental hygiene programs into the routine of health service must wait upon a better definition of the problem, an increase in fundamental knowledge, the development of administrative technique, and a public willingness to spend relatively large sums of money with no apparent immediate returns.

Cancer. The death rate from cancer is rising steadily and, in terms of the annual number of deaths from this cause, cancer constitutes a public health problem of the first magnitude. In 1900 in the United States (6), the mortality rate from "cancer and other malignant tumors" was 64 deaths per 100,000 population; in 1910 the rate was 76, in 1920 it was 83, in 1930 it was 97, and in 1940 it was 120. Thus the rate has almost doubled in forty years. Part of this increase in the cancer death rate is of course due to the fact that in 1940 there was a greater proportion of older persons, that is, persons of cancer age, in the population than was the case in 1900. But more than this is involved, for even when age-specific rates are calculated, it is found that whereas in 1900 the death rate in persons 55 to 64 years of age was 261 deaths per 100,000 persons, the corresponding rate for 1940 was 370. For persons in the age group 65–74, it was 421 in 1900, and 695 in 1940. As a cause of death, then, cancer is increasing actually as well as relatively. It is at present the second most important cause of deaths in the United States.

The Federal Government has established a National Cancer Institute. This forms a part of the National Institute of Health, United States Public Health Service. Its functions are essentially research in character. A few states, notably Massachusetts, have established cancer control programs as part of the work of the state health department. The larger cities, directly through government or otherwise, have established clinics and hospitals for cancer, and these also conduct research. Collateral to these governmental activities, the universities and foundations are engaged in research in this field.

Research is concerned with the gathering of information as to the cause of cancer, and as to therapy. Control programs approach the subject through health education of the public and encouragement of regular examinations, in the hope that early diagnosis may be obtained.

Perhaps an increased availability of diagnostic and treatment centers, as part of community medical service, might contribute to earlier diagnoses and more effective therapy. But it seems likely that until more specific knowledge becomes available the participation of the average health department in cancer control programs must remain spotty and incomplete.

Heart disease. As is the case with cancer, a part of the increase in the death rate from heart disease is a phenomenon of an aging population. But, also similarly, there is an actual as well as a relative increase in this disease. Comparing age-specific mortality rates from heart disease in 1900 and 1940, death rates from heart disease are lower in the latter than in the former year for each respective age group up to age 35. From then on, recent age-specific rates outstrip by far those that existed in the early part of the century. Thus in the age group 45–54, the mortality rate from heart disease was 173 in 1900 and 280 in 1940, and in the age group 55–64, it was 414 in 1900 and 714 in 1940.

Heart disease, with a general mortality rate of 295.2 per 100,000 population in 1942, is the greatest single cause of death in the United States, and if knowledge for its prevention and control were available and applicable, activities in this field might logically take precedence over all others in the public health program.

Unfortunately, heart disease as a public health problem resembles the problem of cancer in more ways than size and rate of increase. A distressing part of this similarity is lack of knowledge as to prevention. Rheumatic fever, some acute infectious diseases, syphilis, and changes in the arterial system are all known to contribute to conditions that are included in the generic term heart disease. Obviously, it is possible to reduce or eliminate some of the primary contributing conditions; equally obvious is the fact that this is not easy to do.

Health departments seldom engage in programs designed directly for the prevention of heart disease, though their activities directed against the acute communicable diseases and syphilis should, eventually, constitute a contribution. Research and more research are indicated and, in such investigations, factors which are now ill defined, as those related to the increasing incidence of coronary disease, may be discovered. Pending this new knowledge, the average health department has but little foundation on which to build a program.

This not altogether consistent treatment of the various problems and activities of health departments seems to be about as far as the subject may profitably be pursued in the circumstances. It is more than likely that the discussion has included an over-abundance of irrelevant material in those aspects of the subject in which the writer has a particular interest; and probably a note of pessimism has crept into the presentation of certain elements of the programs in special fields. The reader would do well to bear these possibilities in mind.

REFERENCES

1. United States Bureau of the Census. Vital Statistics Rates in the United States, 1900–1940. Washington: Department of Commerce, 1943, Table 12, p. 210.
2. Act of July 1, 1944 (Public Law 410: Ch. 373). The Public Health Service Act.
3. Sims, J. Marion. Presidential Address, American Medical Association, Philadelphia. Transactions of the American Medical Association, 27:91, 1876.
4. Act of July 9, 1918 (40 Stat. L. 886, Ch. 143). An Act making appropriations for the support of the Army for the fiscal year ending June 30, 1919.
5. Act of May 24, 1938 (52 Stat. L. 439, Ch. 267). An Act to impose additional duties upon the United States Public Health Service in connection with the investigation and control of the venereal diseases.
6. These data and those immediately following are from Census Bureau Publications.
7. Hooker, Ransom S., Director of the Study. Maternal Mortality in New York City. New York Academy of Medicine Committee on Public Health Relations. New York: The Commonwealth Fund, 1933, p. 34 *et seq.*

VI

A SUMMARY OF TRENDS AND A
CONSIDERATION OF CERTAIN NEEDS

IN the preceding discussion there has been presented an outline of the development of health services in the United States under government. Comments have been made, and what have appeared to be significant events or tendencies have been pointed out. It is recognized, however, that because of the arrangement of material, perhaps to some extent because of its character, and certainly because of deficiencies in presentation, there has not always been a sharp differentiation between those things that are significant and those that are merely interesting. It would seem, therefore, that if one is to visualize public health in relation to a change in social concepts and economic orders, there must be pulled together a summary of those events, problems, pressures, and principles that have shaped public health in government agencies in the past, and these must be scrutinized as to their probable influence in the future.

A Summary of Certain Trends

One of the first things that stand out is that scientific knowledge as to how a given disease may be prevented or controlled is an essential in public health work. Unless the causation, prevention, treatment, and control of a disease in the individual and in the mass are known, the best-laid governmental and social plans will come to nothing. But the mere fact that such knowledge exists gives no assurance that it can be applied, for its application may be made impossible because of cost of program, diffuseness of problem, and the possibility that control measures might interfere with individual freedom or some strong interest. Further, the availability and even the applicability of knowledge are not the only factors that operate in determining the extent and character of public health practice under government. Also of influence are the limitations under which the knowledge may be applied. These limitations are determined by legal instruments, administrative machinery, and budgets. They are formulated by society, or by government representing society, and may or may not be all that is desirable.

For the application of most of the measures designed to maintain health and control disease, the health department is the recognized agent of government. A health department must, therefore, operate within the legal framework and administrative policies of the government of which it forms a part. This legal framework is made up of the constitution, the laws, and the regulations of the governmental jurisdiction concerned.

The interpretation and amendment of constitutions and laws, and the enactment of new laws in the United States reflect the social philosophy and administrative policies that have, from time to time, been current. Courts in the past, and now, make broad or narrow interpretation of the statutes, and thus affect public health work; or a legislative body may suddenly widen or narrow the field of operation of a given public health agency; or an executive order, on the basis of an attorney general's opinion, can overnight emasculate or add to a federal, state, or local health program.

Until comparatively recently, health activities of the Federal Government rested upon those clauses in the Constitution which vested in that government primary jurisdiction in international and interstate affairs. Federal legislation and appropriations in relation to public health, therefore, have been indirect, and largely incident to the already clearly defined and accepted federal prerogatives and responsibilities in connection with commerce. There is now, however, a newer type of national legislation which, while

not abandoning the indirect approach, tends more strongly to utilize the federal authority implied in the welfare clause of the Constitution. What cannot be encompassed under the one authority
may be accomplished through the other. That these two constitutional authorities for engaging in public health work are accepted
by the executive, legislative, and judicial branches of the Federal
Government is in sharp contrast to the halting steps taken by the
Congress in 1798 when the Act for relief of merchant seamen was
passed.

Two other strong trends that exist in the United States must be
recognized as having had a bearing upon the public health work
of federal, state, and local governments, and as likely to be of influence in the future. First, there has always been, and there is now
more than ever, a trend toward a more powerful Federal Government and, second, there has recently developed a strong trend
toward a more socialistic Federal Government. Directly, through
broad interpretations of the Federal Constitution, and by new
laws, or indirectly through grants-in-aid, parity payments, benefits, and rewards, the Federal Government is assuming prerogatives
and accepting obligations, particularly in the field of social security, that a quarter-century ago were regarded as lying exclusively within the jurisdiction of the states. Pertinent in this connection is the fact that public health activities are more and more being
considered as an integral part of the developing social security
program and are receiving increasing federal attention. Thus the
Federal Government is at present a potent influence in public
health. Perhaps it is more virile than any other area of government
for, as will presently be indicated, many state governments are
static in this field, and leadership has focused in the United States
Public Health Service. The policy of federal grants-in-aid for state
and local health work is becoming increasingly popular, and apparently will be continued in spite of what the opponents of this

principle believe it implies sociologically and in terms of state and local autonomy.

Unfortunately federal health services have always been and still are loosely organized, artificially separated, and overlapping in performance. These organizational and administrative disabilities are important and may cause increasing difficulties in the future, for in some ways they constitute a partial barrier to economical and effective administration. This is particularly the case in the present relationship between the health programs of the Department of Labor and those of the Federal Security Agency. But more important than to nurse this distress, and more practical than to await an ideal situation, is to recognize that, as of today, there is within the Federal Government a principal health agency, the United States Public Health Service, quite competent to guide and absorb future expansion or intensification of federal health work.

Another serious deficiency in federal health administration, and one that affects health services for the country as a whole, is that the granting of federal funds to an individual state is not contingent upon submission by that state of a plan that would provide adequate and continuing local health service to all communities within it. For instance, the amount of federal funds that a state receives is determined to no small extent by its total population. But there is no federal requirement that a satisfactory kind and amount of public health service be extended to the total of the state's population. That not all citizens receive these benefits is evidenced by the fact that nearly a third of the counties in the United States are still without public health service organized by local government or provided through localization of state personnel. Remote health supervision from the state capital or intermittent special clinics cannot satisfactorily be substituted for well-rounded, day-by-day local health service.

In most states the state health departments are reasonably effective in discharging the routine conventional duties with which by law and custom they are charged. In view of the circumstances in which they must function they do highly creditable work. Personnel generally is well trained, energetic, sincere, and sensible. As set forth below, however, practically all state health departments suffer from financial, legal, or administrative handicaps and it does not seem likely that, unaided, they will be able to intensify, improve, and expand their services to the degree that seems necessary.

While the legislatures of many states appropriate funds for assistance of local health departments or for provision of local health service in other ways, there are few state health departments, if any, that do not operate under one or more of the following hardships in extending financial aid to local health programs. 1) Funds so appropriated are not sufficient to permit grants-in-aid to all local jurisdictions or to provide localized health service through detail of state personnel. 2) Even if funds were adequate for cooperative programs with all units of local government, no state in the Union has a completely effective law, as in the case of education, requiring that local governmental jurisdictions participate financially in the provision of adequate health service for its citizens. In the few states where some such legislation is in effect, the tendency is to place a ceiling on the amount that may be expended for this purpose rather than to provide that the amount shall not fall below a certain minimum. 3) Only a few states have attempted to work out a formula for grants-in-aid so that the poorest jurisdiction, having made a financial effort proportionate to its resources, would be assured, through state aid, of at least that minimal level of service considered adequate.

Aside from the matter of funds, the extent to which a state health department can ensure adequate local health service, and the way it provides this service, depends largely upon the character of the civil jurisdiction which, under the law, has permissive authority to collect taxes and expend funds for public health work. In many instances this unit, adaptable for most other purposes of local government, is not suitable for public health administration. It may be either too small in population, or too deficient in financial resources, or both. Where these conditions exist, the state health department attempts to compensate by rendering a considerable amount of direct service. But where it is possible to develop local health departments, direct service by the state is at a minimum except along specialized lines, or in unusual situations.

Where the unit of local government is unsuitable for public health administration, most health departments attempt to provide local health service by the organization of district health departments, or by detailing state personnel to aid a part-time health officer in emergency, or by specialized programs, as in connection with water supplies, hotel inspection, crippled-children programs. The establishment of district health departments and their operation by state or local staffs, or by both, are modern and potentially effective administrative devices, in that they provide for combinations of the resources and health interests of local jurisdictions. The inherent danger of the district is that rarely are the staff or the resources nearly adequate to meet the needs of the population which they are supposed to serve. Many localities in the United States are today classified as having satisfactory health service because they are designated as being within health units under the direction of a full-time health officer, when actually the ratio of personnel to needs in such units is sometimes miserably inadequate.

The extension and more active prosecution of public health programs are not live issues in the legislature or in administrative policies of the average state. Governors tend to take corrective action in dramatic situations, but few of them understand the day-by-day work of health departments or have any real interest in it. Politically, the state health officer is relatively an unimportant person and cannot alone overcome this executive and legislative inertia as to public health. It seems unlikely, therefore, that chief executives and legislatures of states will be stimulated to provide more nearly adequate state and local health services unless the matter is made acute through public pressure, through rewards if they participate in a national health program, or embarrassment if they fail to do so.

One of the difficulties in this situation is that state health officers are too close to governors to bring any outside pressure on them. In self-defense some of them appear to have become acquiescent in things as they are. This may account for the fact that many state health officers seem not acutely concerned over a situation wherein large population groups, and large areas of the states for which they are responsible, are without continuing, constructive localized health work.

The respective local authorities of at least one-fourth of the population of the United States have so far failed to provide their citizens with anything approaching adequate health service. It would appear that small communities are unable to provide this sort of service either because it is too big, too costly, or too complex for local initiative to solve, or because that initiative has been dissipated or has been sapped by the tendency of large governmental units to drain authority and responsibility from smaller ones. In the circumstances, it seems unlikely that either the organization of effective local health work in those communities not now so served, or the incorporation of newer services into already operating health departments, will be brought about by local impulse alone. What has caused this somewhat pernicious anemia of small units of government is of real significance sociologically and politically, but from the standpoint of public health practice and planning it is of immediate importance to recognize that progress in extending and improving local health work will, with few exceptions, be interminably slow without more forceful, perhaps more forcible, leadership and assistance from outside.

Measures that Might Well Be Considered for the Future

Choosing the hazards of triteness rather than the dangers of prophecy, it may be said that to develop an effective public health program for the future, action must be along one or more of the following lines:

1. Extension of basic health services to the citizens of every community in the nation.
2. Modification of the individual elements that make up to-day's basic health services, through improvement in quality and effectiveness and by intensification or limitation, as may be indicated.
3. Incorporation of additional services, as new problems, scientific knowledge, administrative techniques, and public attitude make them necessary or possible.

Two fundamental questions are immediately suggested by these possible lines of development, and each has within it a host of subquestions. First, in what sequence should the above procedures be undertaken, and second, how?

It is obvious that neither the second nor the third procedure as listed above may be instituted in local areas in which there is not, as yet, a mechanism for rendering even elementary health service; and a national policy, or even a state policy, preoccupied with searching for the new, or for a refinement of the old, will be questionable as long as there remain vast areas and millions of people without basic and conventional health care. In the circumstances it seems impossible to escape the conclusion that the next urgent step in public health administration in the United States is to provide effective public health service under government auspices in every community of the nation. Once it is done, one may, with logic and conscience, consider building into this minimum program such specialized activities and new undertakings as may be necessary and possible in a changing order.

Whether the second step in improving public health service should be through modification of the conventional elements that make up today's basic health service, or through incorporation of new services, is a matter upon which no decision on a national basis would be sound. The great area of the United States, the different conditions that exist in its forty-eight states and thousands of communities, are such that no detailed and fixed master scheme in relation to second, third, and subsequent steps will fit every community.

It seems wise to re-emphasize here that no plan for improvement of public health services in the nation as a whole or in any given state may be approached, realistically, without a recognition of the fact that the administration of a public medical care program may become the responsibility of the health department. If this should come to pass, much that is done in one way now would then be done in another. Many comfortably established routines would be rudely shaken and it is possible that an hypertrophied medical-care tail would soon wag the none too robust public health dog. But the discussion of that matter is beyond the scope of this presentation. It is within that scope, however, to call attention to the possibilities of such a qualitative and quantitative change in health department responsibilities and to note that a public medical care program would need an administrative mechanism just as badly as does the present conventional public health program.

If one accepts the matter of providing local health services, conventional and then new, to all communities of the United States, as the urgently needed next step in public health administration, then any plan for progress must be laid down to meet known deterrents, on the one hand, and to harness and utilize trends and potentialities, on the other.

As previously stated, the known deterrents include the following: *

1. Authority to expend funds for public health purposes is quite often vested in units of local government unsuitable for sound and economical public health administration. This is seen more frequently where the township is the unit of local government, but not all counties are satisfactory in this regard.
2. In contrast with the situation in relation to education and certain other functions of government, the provision of an efficient health service in the community is a matter of option, to be decided upon solely by local government.
3. State subsidies for aid in providing health service in local units of government are inadequate in most states.
4. In most states, there exist no clear-cut formulas for effective distribution of state and federal public health funds on an equalization basis to local units of government, or for localization of state personnel.
5. There is unfortunate acquiescence, by most state health officers, in the belief that local health service in all jurisdictions in the state can be brought about only gradually and by opportunism and compromise.
6. Many state health officers appear not to be acutely concerned with the large proportion of the population not reached by efficient local health service.
7. There is a tendency in some state health departments to utilize federal grants for building larger central organizations rather than for the extension of local health services.
8. Federal health agencies do not make granting of funds contingent upon submission of an over-all plan by the state for application of federal funds in all local jurisdictions.

* In a few states, but very few, there are occasional exceptions on one count or another.

9. Federal health organizations are scattered, and in some instances there are both duplication of effort and uneconomical administration.
10. Federal funds provided for state aid are inadequate for a nation-wide, federal-state-local health program.
11. The enticing but treacherous comfort of laissez-faire is an undramatic but real obstacle.

No sane person would claim that these difficulties are not real or that they may be overcome without effort.* On the other hand, only a defeatist would contend that they are insurmountable. It is rather obvious that even though in recent years there has been an increase in amount of federal funds for state aid, the goal of reasonably adequate health service in all communities is still far from attainment. Further, it must be recognized that those local jurisdictions which now possess such service are generally the ones which occupy favorable economic situations. The units of government to be reached in the future are in the main local jurisdictions which are sparsely settled or very small or very poor or very remotely located, or very smugly stewing in the juice of their own tradition. The old methods of exhortation and salesmanship do not appeal to them. They can be reached only by a new and different approach.

No one may lay down in detail any scheme which would be applicable in all the states, but three necessities stand out clearly if all communities in the nation are to be supplied with local health service. The first is that federal subsidies for health work be granted to a state only if that state submits an over-all plan which will ensure effective local health service in each of its local jurisdictions. The second necessity is mandatory state legislation, requiring that

* The discussion which immediately follows is based upon that contained in a previous article by the writer: Harry S. Mustard. Need of More Adequate Public Health Programs in the Several States, American Journal of Public Health, 32:957, September 1942.

every unit of local government participate financially in providing its citizens with an effective local health service. The third necessity is state legislation that would require, when necessary, combined administration of the public health activities of local units of government so that service might be performed on an economical basis and with reasonable completeness.

As concerns the federal requirement, it would appear to be neither unconstitutional nor contrary to present trends for the Federal Government to exercise its power to the end that in the several states which accept federal grants-in-aid all citizens receive benefits, thus preventing federal funds from being distributed in a selective, haphazard, or opportunistic manner. Possibly this requirement would be assured by regulations of the Surgeon General and the Chief of the Children's Bureau in relation to the administration of Titles VI and V of the Social Security Act. Certainly it could be effected by amendment to these sections of that Act.

If prompt action is to be obtained there must be some time limit for compliance with such federal requirements. If and when the plan is put into effect, it might be required that a state, to be eligible to receive a grant for improvement of state and local health service, must, by previous legislative enactment or by enactment of the next coming legislature, provide the necessary legal instrument for ensuring state-wide local or localized health service, and further provide a state appropriation which, when added to that state's fair share of federal funds, would be sufficient in amount to ensure such effective local health service. Obviously, it would contribute to ease and economy of federal and state administration and would get rid of much confusion and duplication of personnel and effort if, in this process of federal planning, the amazing and distressing separateness of the United States Public Health Service and the health activities of the Children's Bureau could be corrected.

To provide funds in a nation-wide scheme of this sort, the matter might be approached on the basis of a three-way responsibility. Assuming for purpose of illustration a local budget of one dollar per capita, the Federal Government might then appropriate for local health services in the whole nation an amount in dollars equal to one-third of the estimated population of the United States; the state would appropriate for local health service in dollars an amount equal to approximately one-third of its population; the local jurisdictions would, for local service to be rendered their citizens, provide an amount in dollars equal to approximately one-third of their respective populations.

As both federal and state grants would in effect be equalizing funds, the total of federal moneys would not be divided altogether on a population basis, nor would funds of the state be so divided. A state might get from the Federal Government an amount, in number of dollars, somewhat less than one-third of the state population, and from joint federal and state funds a district or other local jurisdiction, through which health service is rendered, might receive more or less than two-thirds of the amount to be budgeted. The direction of the fluctuation would depend upon the needs and resources of the state or local areas in question.

In connection with mandatory legislation in states, many will say that the citizens and the assemblies of the states would balk at a law requiring an effective level of health service in all communities. Probably in some states this would be the case. However, faced with loss of federal funds unless such funds were used for the benefit of all citizens of the state, probably only a few legislatures would remain adamant, especially as laws requiring a decent local health service would on their merits meet with popular support. And such legislation would be no new thing in state government. Every community is required to have a sheriff or police, courts of law, and a school system, among other things. Also, in the history of the de-

velopment of public health administration in the United States, as
has been recounted, the natural sequence of events has been, first,
permissive legislation as to a board of health and a part-time
health officer, next the gradual acceptance of this permissive legislation by a number of localities, and finally mandatory legislation
as to these primitive necessities. At present, local governments
choose whether or not they will organize *effective* local health
service. The time has come to follow precedent and make the provision of effective local health service a *requirement*.

The mandatory state legislation in question, however, would in
some way have to define what constitutes effective local health
service, perhaps in terms of per capita expenditure for such services. An example of one dollar per capita was used above. It might
be more; at present it is much less. Also, it would be necessary to
provide some formula whereby the amount of funds provided by
each local government of a state, for local health service, would be
proportionate to the financial resources of that jurisdiction. Possibly it might be required that each jurisdiction set aside a certain
proportion of its tax income. Further, in such legislation it would
be necessary to provide that the local unit of government, having
made the necessary appropriation, would have assurance that the
state health department, through funds derived from the state legislature and other sources, would subsidize each local budget in
sufficient amount to build local health service up to a level previously defined as effective. The exact provisions and requirements
in legislation of this sort would naturally vary from state to state,
but so long as the legal instrument provided brought the necessary results, such variations would not be detrimental but rather
the contrary.

Only after taking the step of providing local health service to
all communities of the nation can the nation as a whole think in
terms of engaging upon new activities. This would not, of course,

prevent those state, city, and other local health departments that are already well organized and adequately functioning, from planning programs in nutrition, mental hygiene, control of cancer, heart disease, or similar serious problems of public health. But in undertaking these ventures, let them be sure that all is well in their basic services, that they are not being enticed by the pressure of special-interest groups, that enthusiasm is not carrying them beyond the bounds of available and applicable scientific knowledge. Decisions on these things can be made by states and localities without interference with a national scheme. The latter, it would seem, must primarily be concerned with the extension of basic health services to all citizens of the nation. And in that concern, and in plans that arise from it, there must ever be kept in mind the possibility that the structure and function of all governmental health agencies may need to be changed radically should the delivery of public medical services become a responsibility of health departments.

APPENDIX

TWO HISTORICAL DOCUMENTS

APPOINTMENT OF A HEALTH OFFICER

(Act of the General Assembly of the Province of Carolina, June 7, 1712)

An Act for the More Effectual Preventing the Spreading of Contagious Distempers. /

TA
N° 26
Preamble
N.C.
N°. 11.
N°
317
a health officer
appointed

Whereas, great Numbers of the Inhabitants of this Province have been Destroyed by Malignant, Contagious Deseases Brought here from Africa, and Other Parts of America to Prevent which, as Much as May be, for the time to Come / *Be It Enacted,* by The Pallatyne, and the Rest of the True and Absollute Lords, Proprieters of Carolina To geather with the advice, and Consent of the Members of the Generall Assembly, now Mett at Charles Towne for the South west part of this Province, And it is hereby Enacted by the Authority of the Same, that from, and after the Ratification of the Act, that Gilbert Guttery, Shall be, a Commissioner for Enquireing into the State of health of all Such persons as Shall be aboard Any Ship or Vessell Arriveing in this Province.

His power,
on board
vessels

Be it further Enacted by the Authority aforesaid that the Commissioner aforesaid Shall have Power, and he is hereby Impowred, and Required to goe Onboard of all Ships and Other Trading Vessells, as Soon as they Come Over the Barr, and Make Strict, and Deligent Enquiry into the State of health of that Place from Whence Such Vessel Last, as Likewise of all those persons who are, now Onboard, and into the Causes of the Death of Such as have Dyed Onboard the Said Shipp (if aney) Dureing the Voyage and Shall Make Such Search as, betwixt Decks or in Other Places of the Vessell as is Nessasary for findeing Out the truth,

and Shall Likewise Order all the Menn to be Brought
upon Deck the better to be Vewed, and Observed for
the Same Purpose,

*May send persons
from vessels to the
pest house*

Be it further Enacted by the Authority
aforesaid, That the Comission Aforesaid Shall
have Power and he is hereby Impowred, and Required to Administer an Oath to the Marster, and
One Or two Menn more of Every Ship for Discovering the State of health of those Onboard, Dureing the
Voyage, and at that Pressent Time Particularey who
have Dyed, Or are now Sick Onboard, And ∧ : what
of
Diseases, And it is hereby *Enacted by the Authority*
aforesaid that if the Commissioner, upon Examination findes Cause To send any person then Onboard,
A Shore to the Pest House, The Marster of the Said
Vessell Shall Send them there, and Shall Cleanse the
Vessell, and the Cloaths And Other things of them
onboard after Such Manner as he Shall be Directed
by the Commissioner above Mentioned.

Enacted
Be it further ∧ by the Authority aforesaid, that

*In case of
deaths by
malignant
disorders
to order
the vessel
to lie off
for 20 days*

if it appear to the Comission∧er above mentioned
upon Examination, that Aney person On board the
Said Ship, is sick of the Plauge, Smal Pox, Spotted
Feavour, Siam Destemper, Guinea Feavour, Or aney
Other Malignant Contagious Disease, or That aney
Person Dureing the Present Voyage, hath Dyed
of the
from On board the Said Ship, of aney ∧ Destempers,
aforesaid, he then Shal Order the Marster, or Com-
andᵣ of the Said Vessell, to Send all Sick persons,
then Onboard, or who May after that become Sick
On Shoar to the Pest House On Sullivants Island,
and Shall Order the Marster or Comander aforesaid
to Lye with, his Ship at Anchor, without Sending his
boat a Shoar, Except to Sullivants Island, nor Suf-

fer Aney to Come Onboard his Said Vessell from
Aney Place of this Province Dureing the Space of
Twenty Dayes after those Orders are Given, Dureing which time the Marster or Comand. is hereby Required to Cause his Ship, and things On board to be
Cleansed, after Such Mannor as by the Said Comissioner is Directed,/.

Be it Likewise Enacted by the Authority
aforesaid, That if any person after the Ratification
of this Acte Shal Resist, the Comissioner hereby Appointed, in Performing his Duty, or Shall hinder
him to Come On board, and Search, or Shal Refuse to
Make Oath, as is by this Act Appointed, Or Shall not
Cleanse his Ship as is Directed, Or Shal Refuse to
obey the Orders of the Comissioner, in Sending the
Sick ashore, and hindring his boate from goeing On
Shoar, Or ∧ aney : Others to Come Onboard of him, Every
Person Offending, in Aney of those Particulors Shall
for Each Offence So Committed, forfiet and pay the
Sum of, One hundred Pounds, Currant Money of
this Province, to be Recovered by him or them who
Shall Sue for the Same by Bill Plant or Information
in Aney Court of Record of this Province/.

Be it further Enacted by the Authority
aforesaid that after the Ratification, of this Act, no
Pilot belongeing to this Province, Shal Suffer aney
person, besides himself to Goe Out of his boat On
board of any Shipp Or Vessell, Which hath Come
from any Port Lying to the Southward of the Thir-
tieth Degree of Northern Latitude, and if upon Enquiry, Or Observation the Said Pilot hears or hath
the Least Reason to Suspect that aney Distemper is
Onboard the Said Ship he Shall Wash himself, and
his Cloaths, before he Come On Shoar, and if any
more then One person be put or Sufferd to goe Onboard of aney Vessell Coming from aney Place to

Disobedience
to the orders
of the Health
Commiss^r
to be punished
by a fine
of 100 £

Duty of
the pilot

the Southward of the Latitude, Above Mentioned
Out of any Pilott Boat, or if the Pilot who hath gon
Onboard of Such Vessell, Do Come on Shoar before
he hath Washed himself, and his Cloaths, he Shal
forfeit and pay the Sum of Twenty Pounds, to be
Sued for and Recovered as is above Directed,

Be it further Enacted by the Authority
aforesaid that if aney Inhabitant of this Province, or
aney Person belongeing to aney Ship or Vessell Lying or being Within aney part of this Province, Shal
after the Ratification of this Act, Goe Onboard, of
Aney Ship or Vessell Whatsoever, before the Comissioner, above Mentioned hath been Onboard, and
hath affixt Notice on Som Publick Place in Charles
Towne, that those On board the Said Vessell were in
Such a State of health, as they were Allowed to
Come, and bring the Vessell to Charles Towne,
Every Person so Offending Shal Forfeit, and Pay
the Sume of, One hundred Pounds, Currant Money,
to be Recovered after the Method, and for the Same
use as is above Appointed, but if Such Person goeing
Onboard Aney Ship or Vessell as aforesaid, be unable to pay the Said Sum and be Not a Freholder nor
reputable House Keeper, or be Servants, Negroes or
the Like Inferior People, they Shall be forth with
Publickly Whipt through the Streets of Charles
Towne, upon information, Made to the Governer, or
in his Absence to any Justice of the Pease, who is
hereby Required, after haveing heard, and found the
persons Accused to have been guilty of haveing Gon
on Board Contrary to this Act, to Issue Out a Warrant to the Provost Marshal to Cause, Execution to
be Don, against the Said Offendors According to
this Act, and the Provost Marshal for the time being
is hereby Required to Execute Such Warrant Ac-
cordingley.

No person
to visit
a vessel till
the health
Commissioner
hath been on
board.

under
penalty
100 £

or be publickly
whipt

no master of a vessel to send his boat ashore before the Commissioner hath visited the vessel

Be it further Enacted by the Authority aforesaid, that if aney Marster of a Shipp Or Other Vessell, Comeing into this Colony, after the first Day of March Next Ensueing the Ratification of this Act Shal Send his boat On Shoar upon Aney Place of this Province, or Shall Sufferr Aney Person to Come On board of him, Except One Pilott to Conduct his Vessell in, before the Commissioner, above Mentioned, hath been On board the Said Vessell, and there done What he is Required to Doe by this Act, Every Marster or Comander of a Ship or Vessell so Offending Shall for Every Such Offence Forfeit, and

on penalty of 50 £

Pay the Sume of Fifty Pounds, Currant Mony of this Province, to be Recovered for the use of him or them who Shall Sue for the Same by Bill Plants or Information, in Aney Court of Record within this Province, and wherein no Essoign, Protection, Wager of Law or Stay of Prosecution Shal be allowed or Admitted of *Be it Likewise Enacted* by the Authority Aforesaid that from, and after the Time above Mentioned, all Negroes or Other goods of what Kinde Soever, that Shall be putt on Shore on any Place in this Province, before the Vessell that Imported, Such Negroes or goods, be Viewed by the Commissioner Appointed by this Act, and the Marster thereof Complied with his Orders if he give any Such Negroes or Other Goods, Shal be forfeited to him or them who Shall Sue for the Same, after the Manner aforesaid.

no person to leave the pest house with.ᵗ leave of the Com -missioner

Be it further Enacted by the Authority aforesaid that if any Person or persons, who Shall be put On Shoare at the pest House, on Sullivants Island, Either for Sickness or Suspision of being Sick, of aney Contagious Distempor, Shal goe from thence to aney Other Place of this Province, Without a Certificate first Obtained from the Comissioner aforesaid of his health, and

on penalty of
30 £

haveing Cleansed himself, and Cloathse, According
to the Intent of this Act, Every person so Offending
Shal forfeit and pay the Sume of Thirty Pounds
Currant money to be Sued for and Recovered as is
above Sum Directed or if a negroe or Other Inferior
person offend, he Shall be Publickly Whipt after the
Manner before Appointed.

Be it further Enacted

commr̄ not to per-
mit any of his
company to go on
board till
he is satisfied
the vessel is
healthy

by the Authority aforesaid that the Comissioner
above Mentioned Shal not Suffer Aney of his Company to Goe Onboard any Ship or Vessell besides
himself, before he is well asured of the perfect health
of those On board, and if he findes or Suspects any
Sickness he Shal Change his Cloaths, & Cleanse
himself after the best manor he Can, before he Re-
turnes On Shore upon Aney Place in this Province.

Be itt further Enacted

Commissioner to
examine and give
orders about
the pest house.

by the Authority aforesaid that the Commissioner
Appointed by this Act, Shal Enquire, What is Want-
ing, about the pest House from time to time, Either
for agreing, with Nurses, Makeing Repairs, or Other
Conveniances for the Sick, and Shal aply himself to
the Publick Receiver, who is hereby Impowred, and
Required to Order the Same to be Don, and to Pay
Out for that Purpose Aney Sum, Nott Exceeding
fifteen pounds, a year.

Be itt further Enacted

Persons ordered
to the pest house
are to main
-tain themselves.

by the Authority aforesaid that those who are put
into the pest Hous on Sullivants Island and are of
Ability to Mantain themselves, Shall Doe it at there
Own Proper Charges, That Ancient Infirm poor
people, Shall be Maintained at the Expence of the
Marster of that Vessell which brought them in, That
White Servants, Negroes, and Other Slaves Shal be
Maintained at the Charge of their Respective Mars-
ters, and that the Commissioner above Named Shall

see, That Provisions, and al Nessesary's be Carried
to the Pest House aforesaid, at the Market Price for
the use of Such as are there, and if aney person who
is hereby Required to pay for the Same, Doe Refuse
or Neglect so to Do. The aforesaid Commissioner
Shall always before Such Sum Exceed forty Shil-
lings Procure A Warrant from a Justice of the Peace,
and Recover the same as by the Act for Deciding of
Smale and Mean Causes is Directed.

Salary of
the Commissioner
40 £ per
annum.

Be it further Enacted, That a Salary of
Forty Pounds a year Shal be paid Out of the Publick Treasurey of this Province, to the Comissioner
above Named at Foure Equal Quarterley Payments,
and the Receiver for the time Being is hereby Required to pay the Same.

Commr.
to take
an oath

Be it Likewise Enacted by the Authority
aforesaid that before the Commission:ʳ above
Named or any Other who May Succeed in that Office, Shall take upon them to Execute the things Prescribed by this Act, or be Entituled to the Salary
herein Appointed he Shall take An Oath before the
Right Honble the Governer for the time being, faith-
fully to perform Every thing which he is Impowred

Provision in
case of death.

& Required to Do by this Act, *Be it Enacted* by the
Authority aforesaid that in Case of the Death or
Surrender of the Comissioner afore mentioned, or
for not Duely performing his Duty Another Shall be
Nominated & Appointed by the Generall Assembley,
which if Not then Sitting, by Order of the Governor
and Councill, and the person So Nominated by the
Governer, and Councill Shall Continue till the Next
Sessions of the General Assembly, and Shall have
all the Powers, and Benefitts and be under the Same
Restrictions, as the Comissionʳ before Appointed is
by this Act.

This act to be
confined to the
port of Charleston
but the Gover-
-nor may direct
as to other ports.

Be it further Enacted, by the Authority
aforesaid, That Nothing in this Acte Shall be Construed to Extend, to Aney Other Law full Tradeing
Port which Either now is or hereafter may be Appointed in this Province, besides the Port of Charles
Towne, But that the Right Honab.^le the Governer,
or the Governer for the time being Shall be Impowred, and is here by Prayed to take Care of the
Said Ports According to the true Intent & Meaning
of this Act, as Near, as Circumstances will Permitt,
untill further Provision be made for that Purpose
By the Generall Assembly.

Be it further Enacted
by the Authority aforesaid, that all Actions brought
                        any
upon ∧ Part of this Act, Shal, be prosecuted within
Two years after the Offence Comited, or Otherwise,
Such Actions Shall be Esteemed & are hereby Declared to be vexacious & Illegal.

Be it further Enacted,
by The Authority aforesaid, that this Act and Every
Part Thereof Shall Remaine in force for two years,
after the Ratification there of and after that to the
End of the first Session of the Next Generall Assembly

Read three times & Ratifyed   Charles Craven
In Open Assembly the Seaventh
Day of June Ann. Dom 1712
                                           Charles Hart

    Note   Sect. 12 of
        Repealed by ∧ Act of   Arthur Middleton
    Sep. 1. 1721 on the same subject

                                           H. W. Broughton
                                           Rich:^d Beresford
                                           Sam Eveleigh

FIRST STEP IN THE ESTABLISHMENT OF THE UNITED STATES PUBLIC HEALTH SERVICE

(Report Transmitted to Congress by Alexander Hamilton, April 17, 1792)

> The Secretary of the Treasury, to whom were referred certain papers concerning a marine Hospital at the town of Washington in the State of Virginia, and a memorial of the Marine Society of Boston, on the subject of marine Hospitals, respectfully submits the following Report:

The establishment of one or more marine Hospitals in the United States is a measure desirable on various accounts. The interests of humanity are concerned in it, from its tendency to protect from want and misery, a very useful, and, for the most part, a very needy class of the Community. The interests of navigation and trade are also concerned in it, from the protection and relief, which it is calculated to afford to the same class; conducing to attract and attach seamen to the country.

A fund for the purpose may, it is presumed, be most conveniently derived from the expedient suggested in the above-mentioned Memorial, namely, a contribution by the mariners and seamen of the United States, out of their wages to be regulated by law.

The rate of the contribution may be ten cents per month for each mariner or seamen, to be reserved, pursuant to articles, by masters of vessels, and paid to the collectors of districts, to which the vessels respectively belong. Effectual regulations for this purpose may, without difficulty be devised.

The benefit of the fund ought to extend, not only to disabled and decrepid seamen, but to the widows and children of those who may have been killed or drowned, in the course of their service as seamen.

It will probably be found expedient, besides the reception and accommodation of the parties entitled, at any hospital which may be instituted to authorize the granting pensions, in aid of those who may be in condition, partly to procure a subsistence from their own labor. There may be cases, in which this mode of relief may be more accommodating to the individuals, and, at the same time, more oeconomical.

The Hospital, or if more than one, each Hospital, and its funds, must be placed under the management of a competent number of directors. It is presumed, that for so charitable a purpose, persons will be found, who will be willing without emolument, to execute the trust, but in order to this, it must be rendered as little troublesome as possible, and for this purpose, the number of directors must be considerable. Twenty five, of whom five to be competent to ordinary business, may be an eligible number. Various options will occur to the legislature, as to the mode of constituting the directors, who must, of course, have the power to appoint and compensate certain necessary officers, attendants and servants.

It is suggested in the memorial from the marine Society of Boston, as expedient, to have three Hospitals. But it is not obvious, that one would not for a considerable time, at least, answer the purpose. More would be productive of a greater expense, in the first establishment, and in the subsequent maintenance of it. A plurality would, however, have some advantages arising from the operation of local considerations and feelings.

Preliminarily to a decision, how far it may be expedient to embrace the offer of the marine Hospital at the town of Washington in Virginia, the general principles of the establishment, including the questions of number and locality, will require to be decided by the Legislature.

Should Congress think fit to adopt an arrangement, which will include the town of Washington, as an eligible situation, it will, in the opinion of the Secretary, be advisable, to vest somewhere a power to contract for the building already there. This will probably be found the best mode of reconciling all the considerations which ought to enter into such an arrangement.

All which is respectfully submitted,

Alexander Hamilton

April 17th 1792.
Treasury Department,   Secretary of the Treasury.

INDEX

DATE DUE

DEMCO 38-297